ELON MUSK

In His Own Words

Raphael Afil

IN THEIR OWN WORDS SERIES

ISBN: 9782923241647

www.raphaelafil.com

Foreword

Elon Musk was born June 28, 1971 in Pretoria, South Africa. He was a bookworm who spent a lot of time reading, "I was raised by books, books and then my parents".

Elon once said that ideas are bouncing around inside his head all the time — "It's like a never-ending explosion" — and that he realized he was different from other people when he was just 5 or 6 years old.

"I thought I was insane," he said. As a kid, he worried that authority figures might notice his "strangeness" and put him away somewhere.

Elon lived with his parents in South Africa until the age of eight. When they got divorced, Elon felt sorry for his dad and decided to move in with him. But soon realized that it was not a good idea.

In one interview, Elon described what he said was a miserable childhood. His father was emotionally abusive and hard on his children, allegedly ordering Elon and his brother to sit silent for four hours, as he lectured them. He was such a terrible human being, you have no idea, my dad would have a carefully thought-out plan of evil.

Elon also claimed his father was verbally abusive to him when he was younger, that he didn't believe that Elon will make something of his life and be successful.

Elon was also brutally bullied in school, his classmates pushed him down a concrete stairwell. One time he was beaten so badly that he needed to go to the hospital. They got my best friend to lure me out of hiding, so they could beat me up, and that hurt. For some reason, they decided that I was it, and they were going to go after me nonstop. That's what made growing up difficult.

For a number of years, there was no respite. You get chased around by gangs at school, who tried to beat the hell out of you. When I came home, it would be just as awful there as well. It was very difficult, almost excruciating experiences, both at home and school.

When Elon got his first computer, he immediately got interested in programming and started to learn by himself. At the age of 12, he earned $500 selling a computer game blaster which he created himself.

When he was 17, he moved to Canada to attend Queen's University. I received disapproval from my father, who said rather contentiously that I'd be back in three months, that I'm never going to make it and never going to make anything of myself. He called me an idiot all the time.

Two years later, he transferred to the University of Pennsylvania, where he received an economics degree and a degree in physics. He began a PhD at Stanford University in 1995, but dropped out after two days to pursue an entrepreneurial career. When I was in college, I wanted to be involved in things that would change the world.

He and his brother Kimball founded Zip, a company that provided and licensed online city guide software to newspapers. Four years later, he sold it to Compact for $307 million. He then co-founded PayPal, which became a great success. His first vision of making things easier for people using the digitization. Elon helped to change the financial industry forever. PayPal was sold for 1.5 billion dollars to eBay. Elon held 11.7% of the shares, he received $180 million. He took huge risk with his money, as he invested all in both of his new companies and had to borrow money for rent.

One of them was Tesla Motors, and the second was SpaceX. Both of those companies almost went bankrupt during the recession. But he didn't give up and bounced back. Today those companies are worth billions of dollars. Elon has stated that the goals of SpaceX and Tesla revolve around his vision to change the world and humanity.

Elon is an incredibly hard worker, he once said: work like hell, I mean, you have to put 80-to-100-hour weeks every week. This improves the odds of success. If other people are putting in 40-hour work weeks, and you're putting in 100-hour work weeks, then even if you're doing the same thing, you know that you will achieve in four months, what it takes them a year to achieve. If necessary, he works and sleeps at the factory.

He attacks on the world bests settled markets, as the automotive industry, Elon had declared: we created Tesla to make a difference in the world. Disruption at its best, pushing his competitors forward, expanding and leading technology.

Elon is always thinking about the future of making things work better, more efficient, a visionary man who never gives up. Although there would have been a few moments when giving up would have been a more than plausible option, he never did. He once said: I don't ever give up, I mean I'd have to be dead or completely incapacitated.

For him, SpaceX is not only a business, it's a passion. Many laughed at him. NASA with its billions, the Russians with their ruthless and dead serious ambitions. He stated that goal of SpaceX is to make humanity a space-faring civilization. I think that it is one of the things that makes people excited about the future.

He also declared: I'm trying to allocate my efforts to that which I think would most affect the future of humanity in a positive way.

I think if somebody is doing something that is useful to the rest of society, I think that's a good thing. It doesn't have to change the world. If you're doing something that has high value to people and frankly even if it's just a little game or a system improvement in photo sharing or something, if it has a small amount of good for a large number of people, I think that's fine. Stuff doesn't need to change the world just to be good.

About writing about him and his companies, he once said:

I know there is a bunch of people writing books on Tesla and SpaceX and it is pretty hard for them to get it right, because they just weren't there. Maybe I should write a book of my experiences with all the foolish mistakes I've done and some advice for others that might be helpful.

The goal of this book is to give exclusively to Elon Musk, in his own words, to speak and explain what he thinks, what he wants and how he sees the future.

By listening to him speak and trying to explain his views and ideas, I discovered a man with a sincere goal to change the world and make it a better place. He is not only very intelligent, an excellent businessman, but also very modest and sincere.

California Institute of Technology Commencement speech

(2012)

I would like to thank you for leaving crazy person out of the description, so I thought what's the most useful thing I could say that could actually be helpful, useful to you in the future. And I thought perhaps tell the story of how I sort of came to be here. How did some of these things happen. And maybe there are some lessons there, because I often find myself wondering how did this happen.

So when I was young, I did not really know what I was going to do when I got older, people kept asking me and then eventually, I thought that the idea of inventing things would be really cool. The reason I thought that was because I read a quote from Arthur C. Clark who said that a sufficiently advanced technology is indistinguishable from magic. And that is really true. If you go back, say 300 years, the things that we take for granted today you'd be burned at the stake for. Being able to fly that's crazy, being able to see over long distances, being able to communicate effectively with the Internet and having access to all the world's information instantly from almost anywhere on the earth. This is the stuff that really would be magic, that would be considered magic in times past.

In fact, I think it actually goes beyond that because there are many things that we take for granted today that weren't even imagined in times past. They weren't even in the realm of magic. So that it actually goes beyond that. So I thought, well, if I can do some of those things, basically advanced technology, then that's like magic and I would be really cool.

I had sort of a slight existential crisis because I was trying to figure out what does it all mean? Like, what is the purpose of things. And I came to the conclusion that if we can advance the knowledge of the world, if we can do things that expand the scope and scale of consciousness, then we're better able to ask the right questions and become more enlightened. And that is really the only way forward.

So I studied physics and business because I figured in order to do a lot of these things, you need to know how the universe works and you need to know how the economy works. And you also need to be able to bring a lot of people together to work with you to create something, because it's very difficult to do something as an individual if it's a significant technology.

So I originally came out to California to try to figure out how to improve the energy density of electric vehicles, basically to try to figure out if there was an advanced capacitor that could serve as an alternative to batteries.

That was in 95, that is also when the Internet started to happen. I thought, well, I can either pursue this technology where success may not be one of the possible outcomes, which is always tricky, or participate in the Internet and be part of it. So I decided to drop out. Fortunately, we are past graduation, so I can't be accused of recommending that to you.

I did some Internet stuff, a few things here and there, one of which is PayPal. And maybe it's helpful to say one of the things that was important in the creation of PayPal was which was kind of how it started, because initially the initial thought with PayPal was to create an agglomeration of financial services. To have one place where all your financial services needs would be seamlessly integrated and work smoothly. Then we had like a little feature, which was to do email payments. Whenever we showed the system to someone, we'd show the hard part, which was the agglomeration of financial services, which was quite difficult to put together, nobody was interested. Then we showed people email payments, which was actually quite easy and everybody was interested. So I think it is important to take feedback from your environment.

You want to be as closed loop as possible, so we focused on email payments and really tried to make that work. That is what really got things to take off. But if we had not responded to what people said, then we probably would not have been successful. So it is important to look for things like that, focus on them when you see them and correct your prior assumptions.

Going from PayPal, I thought well, what are some of the other problems that are likely to most affect the future of humanity? It really was not from the perspective of what is the best way to make money, which is OK. But it was really what I think is going to most affect the future of humanity.

I think the biggest terrestrial problem we got is sustainable energy, the production and consumption of energy in a sustainable manner. If we don't solve that this century, we are in deep trouble, and then the other one being the extension of life beyond Earth to make life multi-planetary. The latter is the basis force for space X and the former is the basis for Tesla and Solar City.

When I started SpaceX, I actually initially thought that well, there is no way one could possibly start a rocket company, I was not that crazy. But then I thought, well, what is a way to increase NASA's budget? That was actually my initial goal. So I thought, well, if we can do a low-cost mission to Mars, called Mars Oasis, which would land seeds with dehydrated nutrient gel, and rehydrate them upon landing, you'd have this great sort of money shot of green plants on a red background.

The public tends to respond to precedents and superlatives. This would be the first life on Mars, the furthest that life ever traveled as far as we know. I thought, well, that would get people really excited and therefore increase NASA's budget. Obviously, the financial outcome from such a mission would probably be zero. So anything better than that was on the upside.

I actually went to Russia three times to look at buying a refurbished ICBM because that was the best deal. I can tell you it was very weird going there in, 2001-2002, going to the Russian rocket forces and saying: I would like to buy two of your biggest rockets, but you can keep the nuke, that's (worth) a lot more. That was 10 years ago, I guess that they thought I was crazy, but I did have money, so that was OK.

After making several trips to Russia, I came to the conclusion that actually my initial impression was wrong, because my initial thought was that there is not enough will to explore and expand beyond Earth and have a MySpace kind of thing. But I think that that was wrong, in fact, there's plenty of will, particularly in the United States, because the United States is a nation of explorers, people who came here from other parts of the world. I think the United States is really a distillation of the spirit of human exploration. So if people think it is impossible, that it's going to completely break the federal budget, then they're not going to do it. So after my third trip, I said, OK, well, what we really need to do here, is try to solve the space transport problem and I started Space X. This was against the advice of pretty much everyone I talked to.

One friend made me sit down and watch a bunch of videos of rockets blowing up. Let me tell you, he was not far wrong.

I think it was tough going there in the beginning because I never built anything physical, I mean, I built model rockets as a kid and that kind of thing, but I never had a company that built anything physical. I had to figure out how to do all these things and bring together the right team of people. We did all that and then failed three times. It was tough going, because for a rocket the passing grade is 100% and you do not get to actually test the rocket in the real environment that it is going to be in. I think the best analogy for rocket engineering is like if you want to create a really complicated software, you can't run the software as an integrated whole on the computer it's intended to run on, for the first time you put it all together and write it on a computer, it must run with no bugs, that's basically the essence of it.

So, we missed the mark there, on the first launch I was picking up bits of rocket near the launch site. But we learned with each successive flight and we were able, especially with the fourth flight in 2008, to reach orbit. That was also with the last bit of money that we had, so thank goodness that happened.

I think the fourth time's the charm, so we got the Falcon 1 to orbit and then began to scale it up to the Falcon 9, which is by an order of magnitude more thrust, it is around a million pounds of thrust. We managed to get that to orbit and then developed the Dragon spacecraft, which recently was able to dock and return to Earth from the space station. That was a white-knuckled event, so, yeah, it's a huge relief, can't quite believe it actually happened.

There's a lot more that must happen beyond this, in order for humanity to become a space ranked civilization and ultimately a multi-planet species. That is something I think, vitally important. I hope that some of you will participate in that either at SpaceX or at other companies, because it is just really one of the most important things for the preservation and extension of consciousness. It's worth noting, as I'm sure people are aware, that the Earth has been around for four billion years but civilization, at least in terms of having writing has been around for 10,000 years, and that's being generous. So it is really sort of a tenuous existence that civilization and consciousness as we know it, have been on Earth. I think I am actually fairly optimistic about the future of Earth. So I don't want people to have the wrong impression that I think we're all about to die. I think things will most likely be OK for a long time on Earth, not for sure, but most likely. Even if it's sort of 99 percent likely, a one percent chance is still worth spending a fair bit of effort to ensure that we have backed up the biosphere, planetary redundancy, if you will, I think it is really quite important. In order to do that, there is a breakthrough that needs to occur, which is to create a rapidly and completely reusable transport system to Mars, which is one of those things that's right on the borderline of the impossible. That is sort of the thing we're going to try to achieve with Space X.

On the Tesla front, the goal with Tesla is really to try to show what electric cars can do, because people had the wrong impression. We had to change people's perception of an electric vehicle, they just thought of it as something that was slow, ugly and low range, like a golf cart. That is why we created the Tesla Roadster to show that it can be fast, attractive and long range.

And it's amazing how even though you can show that something works on paper, and the calculations are very clear, until you actually have the physical object and they can drive it, it doesn't really sink in for people. I think it is something worth noting. If you're going to create a company, the first thing to try to do, is to create a working prototype. Everything looks great on PowerPoint, you can make anything work on PowerPoint. But if you have an actual demonstration article, even if it's in primitive form, that is much, much more effective for convincing people. So we made the Tesla Roadster and now we're coming out soon with the Model S, which is a 4-door sedan, because after we made the Tesla Roadster, people said, oh sure, we always knew you could make a car like that, it's an expensive car, low volume, small and all that. But can you make a real car? OK, fine, I'm going to make that, too. So that's coming out soon. That is, I think, the way things are and hopefully that there are some lessons to be drawn there. But I think the overarching point I want to make is that you guys are the magicians of the 21st century, don’t let anything hold you back. Imagination is the limit. Go out there and create some magic. Thank you.

Advice to the Young

There's a lot of technical problems to solve, so I guess studying engineering, physics, biosciences and that kind of thing would be the way to go. They're going to be a lot of problems to solve to make a city work on Mars. We were thinking of just as a semi-joke putting a job description on our website for a “Urban Planner” and in brackets; Mars. But there's going to be a tremendous amount of problems to solve. There will be a lot of building and problem solving so those are like the right skills to work on if someone's interested in going beyond earth, space in general.

The other thing I'd say is that, if you're creating a company or if you're joining a company the most important thing is to attract great people. So either be with or join a group that's amazing that you really respect or if you're building a company you've got to gather great people. All a company is, is a group of people that have gathered together to create a product or service and so depending upon how talented and hardworking that group is, and the degree to which they are focused cohesively in a good direction, that will determine the success of the company. So, do everything you can to gather great people if you're creating a company.

Then I'd say focus on signal over noise. A lot of companies get confused, they spend money on things that don't actually make the product better. So for example, at Tesla, we've never spent any money on advertising. We put all of the money into R&D, manufacturing and design, to try to make the car as good as possible. I think that's the way to go. So, for any given company just keep thinking about these efforts that people are expending, are they resulting in a better product or service? And if they're not, stop those efforts. And then the final thing is, don't just follow the trend.

You may have heard me say that it's good to think in terms of the physics approach, the first principles, which is, rather than reasoning by analogy, you boil things down to the most fundamental truths you can imagine and you reason up from there. And this is a good way to figure out if something really makes sense or if it's just what everybody else is doing. It's hard to think that way, you can't think that way about everything. It takes a lot of effort but if you're trying to do something new, it's the best way to think. And that framework was developed by physicists to figure out counterintuitive things like quantum mechanics, so it's really a powerful method.

I think that the final thing I would encourage you to do is, now is the time to take risks. You don't have kids but as you get older your obligations increase and once you have a family you start taking risk not just for yourself but for your family as well. It gets much harder to do things that might not work out. So now is the time to do that, before you have those obligations. I would encourage you to take risks now, do something bold you won't regret it.

I would advise people to have a high pain tolerance. Maybe there are occasionally companies that get created where there's not an extended period of extreme pain, but I'm not aware of very many of such instances. However, I do think that new great entrepreneurs are born every day and we'll continue to see amazing companies get built. I would definitely advise people who are starting a company to expect a long period of quite high difficulty, but as long as people stay super focused on creating the absolute best product or service that really delights their end customer, if they stay focused on that, if your customers want you to succeed, then you probably will. If your customers love you, your odds of success are dramatically higher.

I think there's a lot of opportunity in general in electrification of transport. Electric aircraft, I think there's a lot of opportunity there. In genetics, although it's a thorny area, I think that's in terms of solving some of the more intransigent diseases, genetics are really key to solving those.

Here's a list of all the dumb things you're about to do, please do not do them. It'd be a very long list and like here, let me write it down or something. It's hindsight's 2020 so it's hard to say. I've made so many foolish mistakes, I have lost count honestly.

If the schedule is long, the design is wrong. We've overcomplicated the design many times and I think we should have just gone with a simpler design. With the acid test being, how long will it take for this to fly? And if it's going to take a long time, don't do it, do something else. You should say no to things that you don't know.

The original Falcon1 team was maybe a little over 100 people. Now SpaceX is like 6,000 people, I think. So really just simplify your product as much as possible. Then think of some of the ways how smart engineer make dumb mistakes? including optimizing something that shouldn't exist, don't optimize something that shouldn't exist. People are trained to do this in college, you can't say no to the professor. The professor is going to give you the exam and you've got to answer all the questions or they will get angry and they will give you a bad grade. So then, you always optimize and answer the questions. A lot of the times you say this is the wrong question. In fact, the question is definitely wrong to some degree, just how wrong?

I think just generally taking the approach is that your design is at some degree wrong, probably a lot more than you think, your goal is to make it less wrong over time.

If something is important enough, you should try. Even if the probable outcome is failure, working crazy long hours, and focusing your efforts to make the world a better place.

Well, I certainly have lost many battles. So far, I have not lost a war. But I've certainly lost many battles. Yeah, more than I can count, probably.

I don't really like risk for risk's sake, I do think that things that are very risky have a low chance of success. But if you want to try to come up with an innovative breakthrough, that's kind of how its going to be. Anything which is significantly innovative is going to come with a significant risk of failure. And you've got to take big chances for the potential of big positive outcome. If the outcome is exciting enough, then taking a big risk is worthwhile. That's really our approach.

But then once executing down a path, to actually do my absolute best to reduce risk, or to improve the product. Another way of saying it, is to improve the probability of success, because when you try to do something that is very very risky, you have to spend a lot of effort trying to reduce that risk as you embark down that path.

When I started SpaceX, I thought the odds of success were very low and most likely to fail. But I thought, well, we should give it a try nonetheless, certainly there are times when things don't go well, then that's quite dispiriting for sure and it's difficult to proceed with the same level of enthusiasm. But I do think that the things we're doing are pretty important for the future. If we don't succeed, then you know, its not so clear what other things would succeed. If we don't succeed, then we will be certainly pointed to as a reason why people shouldn't even try for these things. So I think it's important that we do whatever is necessary to keep going.

Successful entrepreneurs probably come in all sizes, shapes and flavors. I'm not sure there's any one particular thing. For me, some of the things I have described already, are very important. An obsessive nature with respect to the quality of the product is very important. Being obsessive-compulsive is a good thing, and in this context really liking what you do in whatever area that you get into. Given that, you know, even if you're the best there's always a chance of failure.

I think it's important that you really like whatever you're doing. If you don't like it, life is too short, if you like what you're doing, you think about it, even when you're not working, it's something that your mind is drawn to. But if you don't like it, you just really can't make it work.

If you want to do something really innovative, you have to apply a sort of first principles analysis, don't reason by analogy, analogies are referencing the past. Your first principles mean if you look at the most fundamental truths in a particular arena, and the things that really are almost indisputably correct, and you reason up from there to a conclusion. If you see that the conclusion is at odds with what people generally believe, then you have an opportunity.

Now, you can't operate like that on all things because it takes too much mental horsepower. Most operate, by reasoning by analogy, but if you really want to innovate, you must reason by principles to identify the problem.

The reason I came to Stanford was actually to work on energy storage technologies for electric cars. That summer of 95, I was looking at the Internet, and it seemed to me like the internet was going to have a big effect on humanity.

I thought, well, I can either work on electric vehicle technology, do my PhD at Stanford, and watch the internet get votes. Or I could put my studies on hold and try to be part of the internet. At first, I tried to get a job at Netscape because it was the only internet company and they didn't respond to me. So then I was like, okay, if I can't get a job at the only internet company, then I'd better try starting something. I talked to my professor and I said, look, I'm going to try starting a company and its probably not going to succeed. If it doesn't succeed, can I come back? He said, sure no problem. So, I put my studies on hold and started the company.

Tesla came many times close to bankruptcy and In fact, at the end of 2008, we were only a few days from bankruptcy. Literally two days or three days, maybe.

We now know the rest of the story...

Persistence is extremely important

I certainly never expected to see the level of success that occurred because I'm actually an engineer and I discovered that in order to do the engineering that I want to do, I have to have my own company, otherwise somebody makes me do something I don't want to do. I think it's important to apply critical thinking. This might sound trite but to apply critical thinking to what one is doing and by that, I mean just the fundamentals of logic.

Do you have the right axioms? Are they relevant? and are you making the right conclusions based on those axioms. That's the essence of critical thinking, and yet it is amazing how often people fail to do that. I think wishful thinking is innate in the human brain. You want things to be the way you wish them to be in, so you tend to filter information that you shouldn't filter. That's the most common flaw that I see. I also tend to see that people instead of reasoning from first principles tend to act in a mere way, they'll do things because others are doing them because there is a trend. They just see everyone going that direction so they think that must be a good direction to go which is sometimes correct, but then sometimes you know you're going to run off a cliff or something. So, it's much better to really look at things from more of the same physics from a first principle standpoint. What are the fundamental truths or the most fundamental truths in an arena and what conclusions logic that you come to, must be derived from those fundamental truths? Well, I hate to say it but the naysayers do get me down but I think absolutely persistence is extremely important. You should not give up unless you're forced to give up, unless there's no other choice. That principle can be misapplied if you happen to be trying to penetrate a brick roll with your head, so you have to be cautious in always saying one should always persist and never give up because there actually are times when you should give up because you're doing something in error, but if you're convinced that what you're doing is correct then you should never give up.

There's a friend of mine who's got a good saying about starting companies which I think is true. Starting companies is like eating glass and staring into the abyss of death. If that sounds appealing, be an entrepreneur. Actually, that's where physics is really helpful except in unexplored areas of physics or difficult to explore. Physics is very helpful for figuring out whether you're violating one of the fundamental laws like are you conserving momentum and energy if you're not then you probably are not going to be successful or if you think you're not. I think one thing: try to get to a useful prototype as soon as possible with the least amount of money, I think that's usually a good idea. Everything works on power-point and so people are somewhat skeptical if they see a power-point presentation or a website or something but if they see the actual hardware and it's working that is much more convincing. It also will help identify if what you're trying to do is impossible or extremely difficult or something like that. Like I said in the beginning, I'm really primarily an engineer so I enjoy engineering. That's what I derive the most intrinsic satisfaction or happiness from. In fact, I happened to be up until 5 am this morning working on an engineering problem for an improvement to the rocket which I think will be good hopefully, otherwise there's a lot of wasted sleep so I really like working under sharing problems particularly with my engineering teams and coming up with innovative ideas and making them a reality that's what I enjoy the most.

I think certainly being focused on something that you're confident will have high value to someone else and just being really rigorous in making that assessment because people tend to, natural human tendency is wishful thinking so a challenge for entrepreneurs is to say well what's the difference between really believing in your ideals and sticking to them, versus pursuing some unrealistic dream that doesn't actually have merit. That is a really difficult thing to tell, can you tell the difference between those two things? You need to be very rigorous in your self-analysis. I think certainly extremely tenacious and then just work. You just have to put in 80 hours, 80-to-100-hour weeks every week. If other people are putting in 40-hour work weeks and you're putting in 100-hour work weeks then, even if you're doing the same thing you will achieve in four months, what it takes them a year to achieve.

Well, I guess I don't mind taking risks but I think very often people overweight what enjoyment money can bring. Buying lots of things is not necessarily the thing that leads to happiness and certainly being incrementally wealthy does not make one incrementally happy, at least for me it's more like what am I doing that's useful, are my efforts making the world a little bit better, that kind of thing.

I like to build things, to construct and to evaluate my efforts based on what things I have helped to build that people have enjoyed, that's really the main thing. I think that if you look at any big company, you look at the early history, it was always that they had to make progress and I think this is maybe a good general advice for somebody who's creating a company is; try to make something work at a small scale, you prove yourself and then customers will give you a little bit more credit and then you can try something a little bit more. With each successive iteration of the technology, you build confidence, bigger and bigger contracts and that kind of thing.

I think with SpaceX, that's pretty much what happened. We've been able to gradually build the confidence of NASA and commercial satellite operators and that's what's given us the resources to do some additional development like the vertical takeoff and landing. I think it’s certainly important to persist in things.

I do think that there's a framework that physics teaches that's a helpful framework for thinking, to reason from first principles and rather than by analogy, to always question whether you're wrong and try to invalidate your own theories, these are important things.

I also think, maybe people have too much fear of failure. You have to say well what would really happen to you if you failed. You're not going to stop, probably will not lose shelter so why not try things. I think very often people self-limit what they're capable of, without realizing it. I certainly admire Steve Jobs a lot for what he did. He certainly created products that had this amazing feel to them. They just felt somewhat magical and so he did great things with Apple. Benjamin Franklin seemed like someone who did the right thing at the right time. He was a scientist, an inventor, and an all-around good guy. I like generally, scientists and engineers and so at SpaceX for example the conference rooms are named after great scientists and engineers. Obviously, Tesla is named after Nikola Tesla. I think anyone who's done useful things that added to the world, and where you know you'd be sad if that person had not existed, then I think those people are worth admiring.

Podcast With Lex Fridman #1

Lex Fridman: The following is a conversation with Elon Musk. He's a CEO of Tesla, SpaceX, Neuralink, and a co-founder of several other companies. This conversation is part of the Artificial Intelligence Podcast. The series includes leading researchers in academia and industry, including CEOs and CTOs of automotive, robotics, AI and technology companies. This conversation happened after the release of the paper from our group at MIT on Driver Functional Vigilance during use of Tesla's autopilot. The Tesla team reached out to me offering a podcast conversation with Mr. Musk. I accepted, with full control of questions I could ask and the choice of what is released publicly.

I ended up editing out nothing of substance. I've never spoken with Elon before this conversation, publicly or privately. Neither he, nor his companies have any influence on my opinion, nor on the rigor and integrity of the scientific method that I practice in my position at MIT. Tesla has never financially supported my research and I've never owned a Tesla vehicle. I've never owned Tesla stock. This podcast is not a scientific paper, it is a conversation. I respect Elon as I do all other leaders and engineers I've spoken with. We agree on some things and disagree on others. My goal is always with these conversations is to understand the way the guests see the world.

One particular point of disagreement in this conversation was the extent to which camera-based driver monitoring will improve outcomes and for how long it will remain relevant for AI assisted driving. As someone who works on and is fascinated by human-centered artificial intelligence, I believe that if implemented and integrated effectively, camera-based driver monitoring is likely to be of benefit in both the short-term and the long-term. In contrast, Elon and Tesla's focus is on the improvement of autopilot such that its statistical safety benefits override any concern for human behavior and psychology. Elon and I may not agree on everything, but I deeply respect the engineering and innovation behind the efforts that he leads.

My goal here is to catalyze a rigorous, nuanced and objective discussion in industry and academia on AI assisted driving, one that ultimately makes for a safer and better world. And now here's my conversation with Elon Musk.

What was the vision, the dream of autopilot when in the beginning? The big picture system level, when it was first conceived and started being installed in 2014 in the hardware and the cars. What was the vision? The dream?

Elon Musk: Yes, I wouldn't characterize it a vision or dream, it’s simply that there are obviously two massive revolutions in the automobile industry. One is the transition to electrification, and then the other is autonomy. And it became obvious to me that in the future, any car that does not have autonomy, would be about as useful as a horse. Which is not to say that there's no use, it's just rare and somewhat idiosyncratic if somebody has a horse at this point. It's just obvious that cars will drive themselves completely, it's just a question of time. And if we did not participate in the Autonomy Revolution then our cause would not be useful to people, relative to cars that are autonomous. I mean an autonomous car is arguably worth five to 10 times more than a car which is not autonomous.

Lex Fridman: In the long-term.

Elon Musk: Depends on what you mean by long term. But let's say at least for the next five years, perhaps 10 years.

Lex Fridman: So there are a lot of very interesting design choices with autopilot early on. First is showing on the instrument cluster or in the model 3 on the center stack display, what the combined sensor suite sees. What was the thinking behind that choice? Was there a debate? What was the process?

Elon Musk: The whole point of the display is to provide a health check on the vehicle's perception of reality. So, the vehicle's taking information from a bunch of sensors, primarily cameras, but also radar and ultrasonics, GPS and so forth. And then that information is then rendered into vector space, and that with a bunch of objects with properties like lane lines and traffic lights and other cars. And then in vector space that is re-rendered onto a display, so you can confirm whether the car knows what's going on or not by looking out the window.

Lex Fridman: Right, I think that's an extremely powerful thing for people to get an understanding, sort of become one with the system and understanding what the system is capable of. Now, have you considered showing more? So if we look at the computer vision, like road segmentation, lane detection, vehicle detection, object detection, underlying the system. There is at the edges some uncertainty, have you considered revealing the parts that the uncertainty in the system. The instead of. . .

Elon Musk: Probabilities associated with say image recognition or something like that?

Lex Fridman: Yes. So right now it shows like the vehicles in the vicinity, a very clean, crisp image, and people do confirm that there's a car in front of me and the system sees there's a car in front of me. But to help people build an intuition of what computer vision is, by showing some of the uncertainty.

Elon Musk: Well, I think it's, in my car, I always look at the sort of the debug view. And there are two debug views, one is augmented vision, which I'm sure you've seen, where it's basically we draw boxes and labels around objects that are recognized. And then there's what we call the visualize, which is basically a vector space representation summing up the input from all sensors. That does not show any pictures, but it basically shows the car's view of the world in vector space. But I think this is very difficult for normal people to understand, they would not know what the heck they're looking at.

Lex Fridman: So it's almost an HMI challenge through the current things that are being displayed is optimized for the general public understanding of what the system is capable of.

Elon Musk: Yes. If you have no idea how computer vision works or anything, you can still look at the screen and see if the car knows what's going on. And then if you're a development engineer or if you have the development build like I do, then you can see all the debug information. But those would just be like total gibberish to most people.

Lex Fridman: Right. What's your view on how to best distribute effort? So there are three, I would say technical aspects of autopilot that are really important. So it's the underlying algorithms, like the neural network architecture, there's the data that's trained on, and then there's the hardware development, there may be others. But so look, algorithms, data, hardware, you only have so much money, only have so much time. What do you think is the most important thing to allocate resources to? Or do you see it as pretty evenly distributed between those three?

Elon Musk: We automatically get vast amounts of data because all of our cars have eight external facing cameras and radar, and usually 12 ultrasonic sensors, GPS obviously and

IMU. And so, we've got about 400,000 cars on the road that have that level of data. Actually, I think you keep quite close track of it actually.

Lex Fridman: Yes.

Elon Musk: Yes, so we're approaching half a million cars on the road that have the full sensor suite.

Lex Fridman: Yes.

Elon Musk: So I'm not sure how many other cars on the road have this sensor suite, but I'd be surprised if it's more than 5,000, which means that we have 99% of all the data.

Lex Fridman: So there's this huge inflow of data.

Elon Musk: Absolutely, massive inflow of data. And then it's taken us about three years, but now we've finally developed our full self-driving computer, which can process an order of magnitude as much as the Nvidia system that we currently have in the cars. And to use it, you unplugged the Nvidia computer and plug the Tesla computer in and that's it. And in fact, we still are exploring the boundaries of its capabilities. We're able to run the cameras at full-frame rate, full resolution, not even crop the images and it's still got headroom, even on one of the systems. The full self-driving computer is really two computers, two systems on a chip that are fully redundant. So you could put a bolt through basically any part of that system, and it still works.

Lex Fridman: The redundancy, are they perfect copies of each other or?

Elon Musk: Yes.

Lex Fridman: Oh, so it's purely for redundancy as opposed to an arguing machine kind of architecture, where they're both making decisions: this is purely for redundancy.

Elon Musk: Think of it more like it's a twin-engine aircraft, commercial aircraft. The system will operate best if both systems are operating, but it's capable of operating safely on one. So, as it is right now, we can just run we're we haven't even hit the edge of performance. So there's no need to actually distribute the functionality across both SOCs. We can actually just run a full duplicate on each one.

Lex Fridman: You haven't really explored or hit the limit of the system?

Elon Musk: Not yet. The limit, no.

Lex Fridman: So the magic of deep learning is that it gets better with data. And you said there's a huge inflow of data.

Elon Musk: Yes.

Lex Fridman: The thing about driving, the really valuable data to learn from is the edge cases. So, how do you? I mean I've heard you talk somewhere about autopilot disengagements being an important moment of time.

Elon Musk: Yes.

Lex Fridman: To use. Are there other edge cases or perhaps can you speak to those edge cases? What aspects of that might be valuable? Or if you have other ideas, how to discover more and more and more edge cases in driving?

Elon Musk: Well, there are a lot of things that are learned. There are certainly edge cases where say somebody is on autopilot and they take over. And that's a trigger that goes out to our system and says, okay, did they take over for convenience or do they take over because the autopilot wasn't working properly? There's also, like let's say we're trying to figure out what is the optimal spline for traversing an intersection. Then the ones where there are no interventions are the right ones. So you then say okay, when it looks like this, do the following. And then you get the optimal spline for navigating a complex intersection.

Lex Fridman: So there's kind of the common case. So you're trying to capture a huge amount of samples of a particular intersection when things went right. And then there's the edge case where, as you said, not for convenience, but something didn't go exactly right.

Elon Musk: Somebody started manual control from autopilot. And really the way to look at this is view all input is error. If the user had to do input, it does something: all input is error.

Lex Fridman: That's a powerful line to think of it that way. Because it may very well be error. But if you want to exit the highway or if you want to, it's a navigation decision that all autopilots are not currently designed to do, then the driver takes over. How do you know the difference?

Elon Musk: Yes, that's going to change with Navigate on autopilot, which we just released and without stalk confirm. Assuming control in order to change do a lane change or exit a freeway or doing a highway interchange, the vast majority of that will go away with the release that just went out.

Lex Fridman: Yes. So that, I don't think people quite understand how big of a step that is.

Elon Musk: Yes, they don't.

Lex Fridman: So.

Elon Musk: If you drive the car, then you do.

Lex Fridman: So you still have to keep your hands on the steering wheel currently when it does the automatic lane change. So there are these big leaps through the development of autopilot through its history and what stands out to you as the big leaps? I would say this one, Navigate on Autopilot without having to confirm is a huge leap.

Elon Musk: It is a huge leap. It also automatically overtakes slow cars, so it's both navigation and seeking the fastest lane.

So it'll overtake the slow cars and exit the freeway and take highway interchanges. And then we have traffic light recognition, which introduced initially as a warning. I mean on the development version that I'm driving, the car fully stops and goes at traffic lights.

Lex Fridman: So those are the steps, right? You've just mentioned some things that an inkling of a step towards full autonomy. What would you say are the biggest technological roadblocks to full self-driving?

Elon Musk: Actually, the full self-driving computer that Tesla Oracle FSD computer, that's now in production. So if your order any model SRX or any model three that has the full self-driving package, you'll get the FSD computer. That's important to have enough base computation, then refining the neural net and the control software. But all of that can just be provided as an over-the-air update. The thing that's really profound and where I'll be emphasizing at the investor day that we're having focused on autonomy is that the cars currently being produced with the hardware currently being produced is capable of full self-driving.

Lex Fridman: But capable is an interesting word because.

Elon Musk: The hardware is.

Lex Fridman: Yes the hardware.

Elon Musk: And as we refine the software, the capabilities will increase dramatically and then the reliability will increase dramatically and then it will receive regulatory approval. So essentially buying a car today is an investment in the future. I think the most profound thing is that if you buy a Tesla today, I believe you are buying an appreciating asset, not a depreciating asset.

Lex Fridman: So that's a really important statement there because if hardware is capable enough, that's the hard thing to upgrade.

Elon Musk: Yes.

Lex Fridman: Usually.

Elon Musk: Exactly.

Lex Fridman: So then the rest is a software problem.

Elon Musk: Yes. Software has no marginal cost really.

Lex Fridman: But, what's your intuition on the software side? How hard are the remaining steps to get it to where the experience. Not just the safety, but the full experience is something that people would enjoy.

Elon Musk: I think people enjoy it very much so on the highway. So it's a total game changer for quality of life for using Tesla autopilot on the highways. So it's really just extending that functionality to city streets, adding in the traffic light recognition, navigating complex intersections and then being able to navigate complicated parking lots. So the car can exit a parking space and come and find you, even if it's in a complete maze of a parking lot. And then it can just drop you off and find a parking spot by itself.

Lex Fridman: Yes. In terms of enjoyability and something that people would actually find a lot of use from the parking lot. It's rich of annoyance when you have to do it manually, so there's a lot of benefit to be gained from automation there. So let me start injecting the human into this discussion a little bit. So let's talk about full autonomy. If you look at the current level four vehicles being tested on the road, like Waymo and so on, they're only technically autonomous. They're really level two systems with just the different design philosophy, because there's always a safety driver in almost all cases in their monitoring system.

Elon Musk: Right.

Lex Fridman: Do you see Tesla's full self-driving as still, for a time to come requiring supervision of the human being? So it was capabilities are powerful enough to drive, but nevertheless requires a human to still be supervising just like a safety driver is in other fully autonomous vehicles.

Elon Musk: I think it will require detecting hands on the wheel for at least a six months or something like that from here. Really it’s the question of, from a regulatory standpoint, how much safer than a person does autopilot need to be for it took to be okay to not monitor the car. And this is a debate that one can have and then, but you need a large sample, large amount of data so that you can prove with high confidence, statistically speaking, that the car is dramatically safer than a person. And that adding in the person monitoring does not materially affect the safety. So it might not need to be 200 or 300% safer than a person.

Lex Fridman: And how do you prove that?

Elon Musk: Incidents per mile.

Lex Fridman: Incidents per mile.

Elon Musk: Yes.

Lex Fridman: So crashes and fatalities.

Elon Musk: Yes. So, fatalities would be a factor, but there are just not enough fatalities to be statistically significant at scale. But there are enough crashes, there are far more crashes that there are fatalities. So you can just assess where's the probability of a crash, then there's another separate probability of injury. And probability of permanent injury, the probability of death, and all of those need to be a much better than a person by at least, perhaps 200%.

Lex Fridman: And you think there's the ability to have a healthy discourse with the regulatory bodies on this topic?

Elon Musk: I mean there's no question that regulators pay disproportionate amount of attention to that, which generates press, this is just an objective fact. and Tesla generates a lot of press. So in the United States, there's, I think almost 40,000 automotive deaths per year. But if there are four in Tesla, they will probably receive a thousand times more press than anyone else.

Lex Fridman: So the psychology of that is actually fascinating. I don't think we'll have enough time to talk about that, but I have to talk to you about the human side of things. So myself and our team at MIT recently released the paper on functional vigilance of drivers while using autopilot. This is work we've been doing since autopilot was first released publicly over three years ago, collecting video driver faces and driver body. So I saw that you tweeted a quote from the abstract, so I can at least, guess that you've glanced at it?

Elon Musk: Yes, I read it.

Lex Fridman: Can I talk to you through what we found?

Elon Musk: Sure.

Lex Fridman: Okay. So it appears that in the data that we've collected, that drivers are maintaining functional vigilance, such that we're looking at 18,000 disengagements from autopilot, 18,900. And annotating where they are able to take over control in a timely manner. So they were there present looking at the road to take over control. Okay. So this goes against what many would predict from the body of literature on vigilance with automation. Now, the question is, do you think these results hold across the broader population? So ours is just a small subset. One of the criticisms is that there's a small minority of drivers that may be highly responsible where their vigilance decrement would increase with autopilot use.

Elon Musk: I think this is all really going to be swept. I mean the systems are improving so much so fast that this is going to be a moot point very soon. Where vigilance is, if something's many times safer than a person, then adding a person does, the effect on safety is limited. And in fact, it could be negative.

Lex Fridman: That's really interesting. So the fact that a human may, some percent of the population may exhibit a visionless decrement, will not affect overall statistics, numbers of safety?

Elon Musk: No, in fact, I think it will become very quickly maybe towards the end of this year, but I'd say I'd be shocked if it's not next year at the latest, that having a human intervene will decrease the safety. Decrease. Like imagine if you're in an elevator, now it used to be that there were elevator operators and you couldn't go in an elevator by yourself and work the lever to move between floors. And now, nobody wants an elevator operator because the automated elevator that stops the floors is much safer than the elevator operator. And in fact it would be quite dangerous to have someone with a lever that can move the elevator between floors.

Lex Fridman: So that's a really powerful statement and really interesting one. But I also have to ask from a user experience and from a safety perspective, one of the passions for me algorithmically is camera-based detection of just sensing the human. But detecting what the driver's looking at cognitive load, body pose. On the computer vision side, that's a fascinating problem. And there are many in industry who believe you have to have camera-based driver monitoring. Do you think there could be benefit gained from driver monitoring?

Elon Musk: If you have a system that's at or below a human level reliability, then driver monitoring makes sense. But if your system is dramatically better, more reliable than a human then driver monitoring does not help much. And, like I said, if you're in an elevator, do you really want someone with a big lever? Some random person operating an elevator between floors. I wouldn't trust that I'd rather have the buttons.

Lex Fridman: Okay. You're optimistic about the pace of improvement of the system. Now from what you've seen with a full self-driving car computer.

Elon Musk: The rate of improvement is exponential.

Lex Fridman: So one of the other very interesting design choices early on that connects to this is the operational design domain of autopilot so where autopilot is able to be turned on. So contrast another vehicle system that we're studying is the Cadillac Super Cruise system. That in terms of ODD, very constrained to particular kinds of highways, well mapped, tested, but it's much narrower than the ODD of Tesla vehicles.

Elon Musk: It's like ADD.

Lex Fridman: Yes that's a good line. What was the design decision in that different philosophy of thinking where there are pros and cons. What we see with a wide ODD is Tesla drivers are able to explore more of the limitations of the system at least early on. And they understand, together with the instrument cluster display, they start to understand what are the capabilities, so that's a benefit. The con is you're letting drivers use it basically anywhere.

Elon Musk: Anywhere that could detect lanes with confidence.

Lex Fridman: Was there a philosophy, design decisions that were challenging that were being made there? Or from the very beginning was that done on purpose with intent?

Elon Musk: Well frankly, it's pretty crazy letting people drive a two ton death machine manually. That's crazy! Like in the future, people will be like I can't believe anyone was just allowed to drive one of these two ton death machines and they just drive wherever they wanted. Just like elevators, you move the elevator with that lever wherever you wanted. It can stop halfway between floors if you want, it's pretty crazy. So it's going to seem like a mad thing in the future that people were driving cars.

Lex Fridman: So I have a bunch of questions about the human psychology, about behavior and so on.

Elon Musk: I don't know.

Lex Fridman: That would become moot.

Elon Musk: That moot, totally moot.

Lex Fridman: Because you have faith in the AI system, not faith, but both on the hardware side and the deep learning approach of learning from data, will make it just far safer than humans.

Elon Musk: Yes exactly.

Lex Fridman: Recently, there were a few hackers, who tricked autopilot, to act in unexpected ways of adversarial examples. So we all know that neural network systems are very sensitive to minor disturbances to these adversarial examples on input. Do you think it's possible to defend against something like this?

Elon Musk: Oh yes, no problem.

Lex Fridman: For the industry?

Elon Musk: Sure. Yes.

Lex Fridman: Can you elaborate on the confidence behind that answer?

Elon Musk: You know a neural net is just like a bunch of matrix math, you have to be a very sophisticated somebody who really understands neural nets and basically reverse engineer how the matrix is being built and then create a little thing that's just exactly causes the matrix math to be slightly off. But it's very easy to block that by having basically negative recognition. If the system sees something that looks like a matrix hack excluded, it's such an easy thing to do.

Lex Fridman: So learn both on the valid data and the invalid data. So basically learn on the adversarial examples to be able to exclude them.

Elon Musk: Yes, you basically want to both know what is a car and what is definitely not a car. And you train for, this is a car, and this is definitely not a car. Those are two different things. People have no idea how neural nets really, they're probably thinking neural nets involves fishing net only.

Lex Fridman: So as you know, so taking a step beyond just Tesla and autopilot, current deep learning approach is still, seen in some ways to be far from general intelligence systems.

Do you think the current approaches will take us to general intelligence or do totally new ideas need to be invented?

Elon Musk: I think we're missing a few key ideas for artificial general intelligence. But it's going to be upon us very quickly and then we'll need to figure out what shall we do if we even have that choice. But it's amazing how people can differentiate between say the narrow AI that allows a car to figure out what a lane line is and navigate streets versus general intelligence. Like these are just very different things, like your toaster and your computer are both machines. But one's much more sophisticated than another.

Lex Fridman: You're confident with Tesla you can create the world's best toaster.

Elon Musk: The world's best toaster yes. The world's best self-driving, yes to me right now this seems game set, match. I don't want to be complacent or overconfident, but that is just literally how it appears right now. I could be wrong, but it appears to be the case that Tesla is vastly ahead of everyone.

Lex Fridman: Do you think we'll ever create an AI system that we can love and loves us back in a deep, meaningful way like in the movie Her?

Elon Musk: I think AI will be capable of convincing you to fall in love with it very well.

Lex Fridman: And that's different than us humans?

Elon Musk: You know we start getting into a metaphysical question of do emotions and thoughts exist in a different realm than in the physical. And maybe they do, maybe they don't, I don't know. But from a physics standpoint, I tend to think of things, you know like physics was my main sort of training. And from a physics standpoint, essentially, if it loves you in a way that you can't tell whether it's real or not, it is real.

Lex Fridman: It's a physics view of love.

Elon Musk: Yes, if you cannot prove that it does not, if there's no test that you can apply that would allow you to tell the difference, then there is no difference.

Lex Fridman: Right. And it's similar to seeing our world as simulation, there may not be a test to tell the difference between what the real world.

Elon Musk: Yes.

Lex Fridman: And the simulation and therefore from a physics perspective, it might as well be the same thing.

Elon Musk: Yes. There may be ways to test whether it's a simulation. There might be, I'm not saying there aren't, but you could certainly imagine that a simulation could correct, that once an entity in the simulation found a way to detect the simulation, it could either pause simulation, start a new simulation, or do one of many other things that then correct for that error.

Lex Fridman: So when. Maybe you or somebody else creates an AGI system and you get to ask her one question, what would that question be?

Elon Musk: What's outside the simulation.

Lex Fridman: Elon, thank you so much for talking today , it's a pleasure.

Elon Musk: Alright, thank you.

Podcast With Lex Fridman #2

(Nov. 2019)

EM = Elon Musk

LF = Lex Fridman

LF: Let's start with an easy question about consciousness. In your view, is consciousness something that's unique to humans or is it something that permeates all matter? Almost like a fundamental force of physics?

EM: I don't think consciousness permeates all matter.

LF: Pan-Psychists believe that. There's a philosophical....

EM: How would you tell?

LF: That's true. That's a good point.

EM: I believe in the scientific method, don't blow your mind or anything. But the scientific method is like, if you cannot test the hypothesis, then you cannot reach meaningful conclusion that it is true.

LF: Do you think understanding consciousness, is within the reach of the scientific method?

EM: We can dramatically improve our understanding of consciousness. You know, I'd be hard pressed to say that we understand anything with complete accuracy, but can we dramatically improve our understanding of consciousness? I believe the answer is yes.

LF: Does an AI system in your view have to have consciousness in order to achieve human level or superhuman level intelligence? Does it need to have some of these human qualities like consciousness, maybe a body, maybe a fear of mortality, capacity to love, those kinds of silly human things.

EM: The scientific method, which I very much believe in, where something is true to the degree that it is testable so. And otherwise you're really just talking about preferences or untestable beliefs or that kind of thing. So it ends up being somewhat of a semantic question, where we're conflating a lot of things with the word intelligence. And if we parse them out and say, are we headed towards the future where an AI will be able to out-think us in every way? Then the answer is unequivocally yes.

LF: In order for an AI system that needs to out-think us in every way, it also needs to have a capacity to have consciousness, self-awareness and understanding.

EM: It will be self-aware. Yes. That's different from consciousness. What does consciousness feel like? It feels like consciousness is in a different dimension, but this could be just an illusion. If you damage your brain in some way, physically you damage your consciousness, which implies that consciousness is a physical phenomenon, in my view. The thing is that I think are really quite likely is that digital intelligence will be able to out-think us in every way and it will soon be able to simulate what we consider consciousness, to the degree that you would not be able to tell the difference.

LF: And from the aspect of the scientific method, it might as well be consciousness if we can simulate it perfectly.

EM: If you can't tell the difference, and this is sort of the Turing test, but think of a more sort of advanced version of the Turing test. If you're talking to a digital super-intelligence and can't tell if that is a computer or a human, like let's say you're just having a conversation over a phone or a video conference or something, looks like a person makes all of the right, inflections and movements and all the small subtleties that constitute a human. Talks like humans, makes mistakes like a human, and you literally just can't tell, are you really conversing with a person or an AI?

LF: Might as well be human. So on a darker topic, you've expressed serious concern about existential threats of AI, is perhaps one of the greatest challenges our civilization faces. But since I would say, we're kind of an optimistic descendant of apes, perhaps we can find several paths of escaping the harm of AI. So if I can give you three options, maybe you can comment which do you think is the most promising. So one is scaling up efforts on AI safety and beneficial AI research in hope of finding an algorithmic or maybe a policy solution. Two is becoming a multi-planetary species as quickly as possible. And three is merging with AI in and riding the wave of that increasing intelligence as it continuously improves. What do you think is most promising, most interesting as a civilization that we should invest in?

EM: I think there's a tremendous amount of investment going on in AI, where there's a lack of investment in AI safety. And there should be in my view, a company agency that oversees anything related to AI, to confirm that it does not represent a public safety risk. Just as there is a regulatory authority for like the Food and Drug Administration, that's for automotive safety. There's the FAA for aircraft safety, we're generally coming to the conclusion that it is important to have a government referee or referee that is serving the public interest in ensuring that things are safe, when there's potential danger to the public. I would argue that AI is unequivocally, something that has potential to be dangerous to the public and therefore should have a regulatory agency, just as other things that are dangerous to the public, have a regulatory agency.

But let me tell you the problem with this is that the government moves very slowly. And usually when a regulatory agency comes into being, is that something terrible happens. There's a huge public outcry and years after that, does a regulatory agency or rule put in place. It takes something like seat belts: It was known for a decade or more that seat belts would have a massive impact on safety and save so many lives in serious injuries. And the car industry fought the requirements, put seat belts in tooth and nail. That's crazy. And hundreds of thousand people probably died because of that. And they said people wouldn't buy cars if they had seat belts, which is obviously absurd.

Or look at the tobacco industry and how long they fought anything about smoking. That is part of why I helped make that movie, Thank you for Smoking. You can sort of see just how pernicious it can be when you have these companies effectively achieve regulatory capture of government, they're bad. People in the AI community refer to the advent of digital super-intelligence as a singularity. That is not to say that it is good or bad, but that it is very difficult to predict what will happen after that point. And then some probably will be bad, some probably will be good, but if they want to affect that probability and have it be more good than bad.

LF: Well, let me on the merger with AI question and the incredible work that's being done at Neuralink, there's a lot of fascinating innovation here across different disciplines going on. So the flexible wires, the robotic sewing machine that responds to brain movement and everything around ensuring safety and so on. So we currently understand very little about the human brain. Do you also hope that the work at Neuralink will help us understand more about the human mind, about the brain?

EM: Yes. I think the work in Neuralink will definitely shed a lot of insight into how the brain, the mind works. Right now, just the data we have regarding how the brain works is very limited. We've got FMRI, that's kind of like putting a stethoscope on the outside of a factory wall and then putting it like all over the factory wall. And you can sort of hear the sounds, but you don't know what the machines are doing really. It's hard, you can infer a few things, but it's very broad brush stroke. In order to really know what's going on in the brain, you really need, you have to have high precision sensors, and then you want to have stimulus and response. Like if you trigger a neuron, how do you feel? What do you see? How does it change your perception of the world?

LF: You're speaking to physically just getting close to the brain. Being able to measure signals from the brain will give us sort of opened the door and inside the factory.

EM: Yes, exactly. Being able to have high precision sensors that tell you what individual neurons are doing, and then being able to trigger neurons and see what the response is in the brain. So you can see the consequences of if you fire this neuron, what happens? How do you feel? What does it change? It'll be really profound to have this in people because people can articulate their change. Like if there's a change in mood, or if they can tell you if they can see better or hear better, or be able to form sentences better or worse, or their memories are jogged or that kind of thing.

LF: So on the human side, there's this incredible general malleability, plasticity of the human brain, the human brain adapts, adjusts and so on.

EM: It's not that plastic to be totally frank.

LF: So there's a firm structure, but nevertheless, there is some plasticity in the open question is sort of, if I could ask a broad question is how much that plasticity can be utilized? Sort of on the human side, there's some plasticity in the human brain. And on the machine side, we have our neural networks, machine learning, artificial intelligence, it's able to adjust and figure out signals. So there's a mysterious language that we don't perfectly understand that's within the human brain. And then we're trying to understand that language to communicate both directions. So the brain is adjusting a little bit, we don't know how much, and the machine is adjusting. Where do you see as they try to sort of reach together almost like with an alien species, try to find a communication protocol that works. Where do you see the biggest benefit arriving from? On the machine side or the human side? Do you see both of them working together?

EM: I actually think the machine side is far more malleable than the biological side, by a huge amount. So it will be the machine that adapts to the brain, that's the only thing that's possible. The brain can't adapt that well to the machine. You can't have neurons start to regard an electrode like another neuron cause like neurons are like the pulse. And so something else is pulsing so there's that elasticity in the interface, which we believe is something that can happen. But the vast majority of the malleability will have to be on the machine side.

LF: It's interesting when you look at that synaptic plasticity at the interface side, there might be like an emergent plasticity. Cause it's a whole other, it's not like in the brain, it's a whole other extension of the brain. You know, we might have to redefine what it means to be malleable for the brain. So maybe the brain is able to adjust to external interfaces.

EM: There'll be some adjustments to the brain cause there's going to be something reading and simulating the brain. And so it will adjust to that thing, but most of the vast majority of the adjustment will be on the machine side. It has to be that otherwise it will not work. Ultimately, we currently operate on two layers. We have sort of Olympic like prime primitive brain layer, which is where all of our kind of impulses are coming from. It's sort of like we've got like a monkey brain with a computer stuck on it, that's the human brain. And a lot of our impulses and everything are turned by the monkey brain. And the computer of the cortex is constantly trying to make the monkey brain happy. It's not the cortex that's steering the monkey brains, the monkey brains steering the cortex.

LF: But the cortex is the part that tells the story of the whole thing. So we convince ourselves it's more interesting than just the monkey brain.

EM: The cortex is like what we call like human intelligence. So that's like the advanced computer relative to other creatures. Other creatures do not have even, really they don't have the computer, or they have a very weak computer relative to humans. It sort of seems like surely the really smart thing should control the dumb thing, but actually don't think it's a smart thing.

LF: So do you think some of the same kind of machine learning methods whether that's natural language processing applications are going to be applied for the communication between the machine and the brain? To learn how to do certain things like movement of the body, how to process visual stimuli and so on. Do you see the value of using machine learning to understand the language of the two way communication with the brain?

EM: Sure. Yes, absolutely. I mean we're a neural net and AI is basically neural net. So this is like digital neural net will interface with biological neural net and hopefully bring us along for the ride. But the vast majority of our intelligence will be digital. Think of like the difference in intelligence between your cortex and your limbic system is gigantic, your limbic system really has no comprehension of what the hell the cortex is doing. It's just literally hungry or tired or angry or something and then it communicates that, that impulse to the cortex and tells the cortex to go satisfy that. Like a massive amount of thinking, like truly stupendous amount of thinking has gone into sex, without purpose, without procreation, which is actually quite a silly action in the absence of procreation. So why are you doing it? Because it makes the limbic system happy. That's why. It's pretty absurd really

LF: Well. The whole of existence is pretty absurd in some kind of sense.

EM: Yes, I mean, this is a lot of computation has gone into how can I do more of that with procreation not even being a factor. This is I think a very important area of research by NSFW

LF: An agency that should receive a lot of funding, especially after this conversation.

EM: I propose the formation of a new agency

LF: What is the most exciting or some of the most exciting things that you see in the future impact of Neuralink? Both on the science and engineering and societal broad impact.

EM: So Neuralink, I think at first will solve a lot of brain-related diseases. So anything from like autism, schizophrenia, memory loss, like everyone experiences memory loss at certain points in age. Parents can't remember their kids' names and that kind of thing. So there's like a tremendous amount of good that Neuralink can do in solving critical damage to the brain or the spinal cord. There's a lot that can be done to improve quality of life of individuals and those will be steps along the way. And then ultimately it's intended to address the existential risk associated with digital super intelligence. Like we will not be able to be smarter than a visual supercomputer. So therefore you cannot beat them, join them and at least we won't have that option.

LF: So you have hope that Neuralink will be able to be a kind of a connection to allow us to merge, to ride the wave of the improving AI system.

EM: I think the chance is above 0%.

LF: So it's nonzero.

EM: Yes.

LF: There's a chance.

EM: Have you seen Dumb and Dumber?

LF: Yes.

EM: So what I'm saying there's a chance.

LF: You're saying one in a billion or one in a million, whatever it was on Dumb and Dumber

EM: It went from maybe one in a million to improving. Maybe it'll be one a thousand and then one and a hundred, then one to 10, depends on the rate of improvement of Neuralink and how fast we are able to make progress.

LF: Well, I have talked to a few folks here that are quite brilliant engineers, so I'm excited.

EM: I think it's like fundamentally good, giving somebody back full motor control after they've had a spinal cord injury, restoring brain functionality after a stroke, solving debilitating, genetically oriented brain diseases. These are all incredibly great I think and in order to do these, you have to be able to interface with the neurons at a detailed level. Fire the right neurons, read the right neurons and then effectively you can create a circuit, replace what's broken with silicon and essentially fill in the missing functionality. And then over time we can develop a tertiary layer. So if like limbic system is a primary layer, then the cortex is like a second layer. And as I said, the cortex is vastly more intelligent than the limbic system, but people generally like the fact that they have a limbic system and a cortex. I haven't met anyone who wants to delete either one of those. They're like, okay, I'll keep them both. That's cool.

LF: The limbic system is kind of fun.

EM: That's where all the fun is absolutely, people generally don't lose their cortex either. So they like having the cortex and the limbic system. Then there's a tertiary layer, which will be digital super-intelligence. I think there's room for optimism, given that the cortex is very intelligent and limbic system is not, and yet they work together well. Perhaps there can be a tertiary layer where digital super-intelligence lies and that will be vastly more intelligent than the cortex, but still co-exist peacefully and in a benign manner with the cortex and limbic system,

LF: That's a super exciting future, both on low-level engineering that I saw is being done here and the actual possibility in the next few decades.

EM: It's important that Neuralink solves this problem sooner rather than later, because the point at which we have digital super intelligence, that's when we pass the singularity and things become just very uncertain. It doesn't mean that they're necessarily bad or good, but the point of which we've passed singularity things become extremely unstable. So we want to have a human brain interface before the singularity, or at least not long after it to minimize existential risks for humanity and consciousness, as we know it.

LF: So there's a lot of fascinating actual engineering low-level problems here at Neuralink that are quite exciting.

EM: The problems that we face at Neuralink are material science, electrical engineering, software, mechanical engineering, micro-fabrication. It's a bunch of engineering disciplines essentially. That's what it comes down to is you have to have a tiny electrode, so it's so small, it doesn't hurt neurons, but it's got to last for as long as a person. So it's going to last for decades and then you've got to take that signal and you've got to process that signal locally at low power. So we need a lot of chip design engineers because we've got to do signal processing and do so in a very power efficient way so that we don't heat your brain up, because brain's very heat sensitive. And then we've got to take those signals we're going to do something with them. And then we've got to stimulate them back to bidirectional communication.

So somebody who’s good at material science software, mechanical engineering, electrical engineering, chip design, micro-fabrication, those are the things we need to work on. We need to be good at material science so that we can have tiny electrodes that last a long time and it's a tough thing because you're trying to read and simulate electrically in an electrically active area. Your brain is very electrically active and electrochemically active. So how do you have say a coating on the electrode that doesn't dissolve over time, and is safe in the brain? This is a very hard problem. And then how do you collect those signals in a way that is most efficient? Because you really just have very tiny amounts of power to process those signals. Then we need to automate the whole thing. So it's like Lasik, if this is done by neurosurgeons, there's no way it can scale to large numbers of people and it needs to scale to large numbers of people, because I think ultimately we want the future to be determined, by a large number of humans.

LF: Do you think that this has a chance to revolutionize surgery, period? So neurosurgery and surgery all across the board?

EM: Yes, for sure. It's going to be like Lasik. If Lasik had to be hand done or that done by hand by person, that wouldn't be great, it's done by a robot. The ophthalmologist kind of just needs to make sure your head's in the right position and then they just press a button and go

LF: So smart summon and soon Auto park takes on the full, beautiful mess of parking lots and they're human to human, nonverbal communication. I think it has actually the potential to have a profound impact in changing how our civilization looks at AI and robotics, because this is the first time human beings, people that don't own a Tesla may have never seen a Tesla or heard about a Tesla get to watch hundreds of thousands of cars without a driver. Do you see it this way? Almost like an education tool for the world about AI? Do you feel the burden of that, the excitement of that, or do you just think it's a smart parking feature?

EM: I do think you are getting at something important, which is most people have never really seen a robot. And what is the car that is autonomous, it's a four wheeled robot, right? Yes.

LF: It communicates a certain sort of message with everything from safety to the possibility of what AI could bring to its current limitations. It's current challenges, what's possible. Do you feel the burden of that almost like a communicator educator to the world about AI?

EM: We were just really trying to make people's lives easier with autonomy. But now that you mention it, I think it will be an eye-opener to people about robotics, because they've really never seen, most people never seen a robot and there are hundreds of thousands of Teslas. Won't be long before there's a million of them that have autonomous capability and to drive without a person in it. You can see the kind of evolution of the car's personality and thinking with each iteration of autopilot. You can see it's uncertain about this, but now it's more certain, now it's moving in a slightly different way. Like I can tell immediately if a car is on Tesla autopilot, it’s got just little nuances of movement. It just moves in a slightly different way. Cars on Tesla autopilot, for example, on the highway are far more precise about being in the center of the lane than a person. If you drive down the highway and look at where cars are, the human driven cars are within their lane, they're like bumper cars. They're like moving all over the place, the car on autopilot, dead center.

LF: Yes. So the incredible work that's going into that neural network, it's learning fast autonomy is still very, very hard. We don't actually know how hard it is fully, of course. But you look at most problems you tackle this one included with an exponential lens, but even with an exponential improvement, things can take longer than expected sometimes. So where does Tesla currently stand on its quest for full autonomy? What's your sense? When can we see successful deployment of full autonomy?

EM: Well, on the highway already, the probability of an intervention is extremely low. So for highway autonomy with the latest release, especially the probability of need to intervene, is really quite low. In fact, I'd say for stop and go traffic it's far safer than a person right now. The probability of an injury or an impact is much, much lower for autopilot than a person. And then with navigating autopilot, it can change lanes, take highway interchanges, and then we're coming at it from the other direction, which is low speed, full autonomy. And in a way, this is like how does a person learn to drive? You learn to drive in the parking lot. The first time you learn to drive, probably wasn't jumping on Market Street in San Francisco, that would be crazy. You learn to drive in the parking lot, get things right at low speed. And then the missing piece that we're working on is traffic lights and stop streets. Stop streets, I would say actually also relatively easy because, you kind of know where the stop street is, worse case you can geocode it and then use visualization to see where the line is and stuff with the line to eliminate the GPS error. So actually, I would say it’s probably complex traffic lights and very windy roads are the two things that need to get solved,

LF: What's harder, perception or control for these problems? So being able to perfectly perceive everything or figuring out a plan, once you perceive everything, how to interact with all the agents in the environment. In your sense from a learning perspective is perception or action harder in that giant beautiful multitask learning neural network.

EM: The hottest thing is having an accurate representation of the physical objects in vector space. So taking the primarily visual input sonar and radar, and then creating the accurate vector space representation of the objects around you. Once you have an accurate vector space representation, the planning and control is relatively easier, it is relatively easy. Basically, once you have accurate vector space representation, then you're kind of like a video game, like cars in like Grand Theft Auto or something like they work pretty well. They drive down the road, they don't crash, you know pretty much unless you crash into them. That's because they've got an accurate vector space representation of where the cars are and they're just there and then the rendering that as the output,

LF: Do you have a sense high level that Tesla's on track on being able to achieve full autonomy? So on the highway.

EM: Yes, absolutely.

LF: And still, no driver sensing?

EM: And we have drivers sensing with torque on the wheel.

LF: By the way, just a quick comment on karaoke. Most people think it is fun, but I also think it is the driving feature, I've been saying for a long time, singing in the car is really good for attention management and visual management.

EM: Tesla karaoke is one of the most fun features of the car.

LF: Do you think of the connection between fun and safety sometimes

EM: Yes. We can do both at the same time that's great.

LF: I just met with Andrew and wife of Carl Sagan. Director of Cosmos.

EM: I'm generally a big fan of Paul Sagan. He's super cool. He has a great way of putting things. All of our consciousness, all civilization, everything we've ever known and done is on this tiny blue dot. People also get, they get too trapped in like squabbles amongst humans. And there's nobody thinking of the big picture. And they take a civilization and our continued existence for granted, they shouldn't do that. Look at the history of civilizations, they rise, and they fall. And now civilization, it's globalized and so every civilization, I think now rises and falls together, there's not geographic isolation. This is a big risk. Things don't always go up, that's an important lesson of history.

LF: In 1990 at the request of Carl Sagan, the Voyager 1 spacecraft, which is a spacecraft that's reaching out farther than anything human made into space, turned around to take a picture of earth from 3.7 billion miles away. And as you're talking about the pale blue dot that picture there, it takes up less than a single pixel on that image. Appearing as a tiny blue dot a pale blue dot as Sagan called it. So he spoke about this dot of ours in 1994. And if you could humor me, I was wondering if in the last two minutes you could read the words that he wrote describing this pale blue dot.

EM: Sure. Yes. It's funny the universe appears to be 13.8 billion years old. Earth, like four and a half billion years old. In another half billion years or so, the sun will expand and probably evaporate the oceans and make life impossible on earth, which means that if it had taken consciousness 10% longer to evolve, it would never have evolved at all. Just 10% longer. I wonder how many dead one planet civilizations there are out there in the cosmos that never made it to the other planet and ultimately extinguished themselves or were destroyed by external factors. Probably a few, it's only just possible to try to travel to Mars. Just barely. If G was 10% more, it wouldn't work really, if G was 10% lower would be easy.

We can go single stage from the surface of Mars all the way to the surface of the Earth, because Mars is 37% of earth's gravity. We need a giant boost to get off the earth. Channeling Carl Sagan, look again at that dot, that's here, that's home, that's us. On it, everyone you love, everyone you know, everyone you've ever heard of, every human being whoever was, lived out their lives, the aggregate of our joy and suffering, thousands of confident religions, ideologies and economic doctrine. Every hunter and forager, every hero and coward, every creator and destroyer of civilization, every king and peasant, every young couple in love, every mother and father, hopeful child, inventor and explorer. Every teacher of morals, every corrupt politician, every superstar, every Supreme leader. Every saint and sinner in the history of our species lived there. On a mote of dust suspended in a Sunbeam.

Our planet is a lonely speck in the great enveloping cosmic dark. In our obscurity in all those vastness, there is no hint that help will come from elsewhere to save us from ourselves. The earth is the only world known so far to harbor life. There is nowhere else, at least in the near future to which our species could migrate. This is not true. This is false. Mars.

LF: And I think Carl Sagan would agree with that. He couldn't even imagine it at that time. So thank you for making the world dream and thank you for talking today. I really appreciate it.

Podcast with Joe Rogan

(2020)

For sure in recent years, billionaire has become a PR job. Like it's a pejorative, like it's a bad thing, which I think, doesn't make a lot of sense.

I think possessions kind of weigh you down. They're kind of an attack vector. You know, he'll say, hey, Billionaire, you got all this stuff like, well, now I don't have stuff now. What are you going to do?

About getting rid of material possessions: I've been thinking about it for a while. Yet a part of it is like, have a bunch of houses, but I don't spend a lot of time in most of them. And that doesn't seem like a good use of assets. Like somebody could probably be enjoying those houses and get better use of them than me. But then I was like, do I really want? Does it really make sense for me to spend time designing and building a house? And I'd be real, you know, get like OCD on the little details and the design or should I be allocating that time to getting us to Mars? I should probably do the latter. So you know, like, what's more important Mars or a house? I like Mars.

In most cases, if you basically organize a company like how to harness, this wealth arises, if you organize people in a better way, to produce products and services that are better than what existed before, and you have some ownership in that company, then that essentially gives you the right to allocate more capital.

So there's a conflation of consumption and capital allocation. Warren Buffett, for example, to be totally frank, I'm not his biggest fan, he does, like capital allocation. And he reads a lot of annual reports of companies and all the accounting, and it's pretty boring, really. And what he's trying to figure out is, does Coke or Pepsi deserve more capital? I mean, it's kind of a boring job if you ask me. It's still a thing that's important to figure out, like, which company is deserving more or less capital, should that company grow or expand? Is it making products and services that are better than others? Or worse, and if a company is making compelling products and services, it should get more capital, and if it's not, it should get less or go out of business.

I do think that in the United States, especially, there's an over allocation of talent in finance and law. Basically, too many smart people go into finance and law. This is both a compliment and a criticism. We should have, I think fewer people doing law and less people doing finance and more people making stuff. Manufacturing used to be highly valued in the United States. And these days, it's not. It's often looked down upon, which I think is wrong. Somebody's got to do the real work, like making a car, or making anything or providing a valuable service. Like providing greater entertainment, good information, these are all valuable things to do. There should be more of it.

AI Neural Net

The essential elements of an AI neural net are really very, very similar to a human brain neural net. Having the multiple layers of neurons and backpropagation, all these things are what your brain does. You have a layer of neurons that goes through a series of intermediate steps to ultimately cognition, and then it'll reverse those steps and go back and forth and go all over the place. It's interesting, very interesting.

For the Neural Link, we're not testing people yet. But I think it won't be too long, I think we may be able to implant a neural link in less than a year, in a person, I think. It's a very low potential for rejection. I mean, you can think of it like people put in heart monitors and things for epileptic seizures and deep brain stimulation, for artificial hips and knees and that kind of thing. So the probability of what will cause rejection what will not? It's definitely harder when you've got something that is sort of reading and writing neurons, that's generating a current pulse and reading current pulses. That's, a little hotter than a dense passive device, but it's still very doable. And yes, there are people who have primitive devices in their brains right now.

Like deep brain stimulation is binding for Parkinson's it has really changed people's lives in a big way. Which is kind of remarkable, because it kind of like, zaps your brain. So this deep brain stimulation implanted devices in the brain have changed people's lives for the better. Like, fundamentally, what happens if someone ultimately gets a neural link installed. Well, for version 1 of the devices that would be basically implanted in your skull, so it would be flush with your skull. If you basically take out a chunk of skull, replace, put the neural link device in there, you'd put the electrode, you'd insert the electrode threads very carefully into the brain. And then you stitch it up, and you wouldn't even know that somebody has it. And then it can interface basically anywhere, anywhere in your brain. It could be something that helps cure, say, eyesight, like returns your eyesight, even if you've lost your optic nerve.

Hearing, obviously, I mean, pretty much anything that it could, in principle fix, almost anything that is wrong with the brain. It could restore limb functionality. To interface into the motor cortex with an implant that's like a microcontroller near the muscle groups, you could then create a sort of a neural shunt that restores somebody who is a quadriplegic to full functionality, so they can walk around like normal. The device we're working on right now is about an inch in diameter. A skull is pretty thick, by the way. I mean, if you're big, if you're a big guy, your skull is actually fairly thick. You would replace say, one inch diameter piece of skull with this euro like device that has a battery a Bluetooth and an inductive charger. Then you also get to insert the electrodes that are carefully inserted with a robot that we developed, that is very carefully putting in the electrodes and avoiding any veins or arteries, so it doesn't create trauma. At the end, they put the device in and that replaces the little piece of skull that was taken out. Stitch up the hole and separate like a little scar. And that's it.

Other possible cognitive benefits

Basically, it's a generalized sort of thing for fixing any kind of brain injury in principle, or if you've got like severe epilepsy or something like that, it could just stop the episode epilepsy from occurring, like it can detect it in real time, and then fire a counter pulse and stop the epilepsy. I mean, there's a whole range of brain injuries, like someone gets a stroke, they could lose the ability to speak, or stroke damage, or if you lose muscle control over part of your face or something like that. And then when you get older, if you get like, Alzheimer's or something like that, then you lose memory, this could help you with restoring your memory, that kind of thing. It's like, think of like a bunch of circuits, there's some that are broken, and we can like fix those circuits that substitute for those circuits. I mean, there's still a lot of work to do. So when I say, we've got a shot at probably putting it in a person within a year, I think we have a chance of putting into one and having them be healthy and restoring some functionality that they've lost.

Essentially, it's just that the data rate to the electronics is slow. Especially output, like you're just going with your thumbs, what's your data rate? Maybe, optimistically, 100 beats per second, that's being generous. Now, the computer can communicate at like 100 terabytes. So certainly, gigabits are trivial at this point. This is like basically if your computer could do things a million times faster. So, if you can solve the data rate issue, output and input, then you can improve the symbiosis that is already occurring between man and machine.

When you let's say, have got some complex idea that you're trying to convey to somebody else. How do you do that? Well, your brain spends a lot of effort, compressing complex concept into words. And there's a lot of information loss that occurs when compressing a complex concept into words. And then you say those words, those words are then interpreted, then they're decompressed by the person who is listening, and they will, at best get a very incomplete understanding of what you're trying to convey. It's very difficult to convey complex concepts with precision because you've got compression, decompression, you may not even have heard all the words correctly. Therefore, communication is difficult. What we have here is a failure to communicate.

Here is another sort of interesting idea, which is, where did consciousness arise? While assuming you believe in physics which appears to be true, then you know, the universe started off as basically quarks and leptons and quickly became hydrogen, helium, lithium, like basically elements, the periodic table, but like mostly hydrogen, basically. And then, over a long period of time, 13. 8 billion years later, that hydrogen became sentient. Where along the way is the line of consciousness and not consciousness? Between hydrogen and here? Well, I hope consciousness propagates in the future, and it gets more sophisticated and complex and understand the questions to ask about the universe.

You don't always improve, but you can aspire to improve, or you can aspire to be less wrong. This is like, I think good tools of physics that are very powerful. Like, just assume you're wrong, and you're asked to go less wrong. I don't think you're going to succeed every day being less wrong. But, you know, if you're going to succeed in being less wrong, most of the time, you're doing great.

There are huge differences in cognitive ability and resources already. You can think of a corporation as like a cybernetic collective. That's far smarter than an individual, like, I couldn't personally build a whole rocket, the engines and launch it, that's impossible. But we have 1000 people at SpaceX and you're piecing it out to different people. Using computers and machines and stuff, we can make lots of rockets launch into orbit, dock with the space station, that kind of thing, so that already exists, as corporations are vastly more capable than an individual. We should be, I think, less concerned about relative capabilities between people and more like having AI be vastly, beyond us, and decoupled from human will.

It's not a requirement to achieve some sort of symbiotic existence with AI. It's just if you want to be along for the ride, then you need to do some kind of symbiosis. So the way your brain works, right now, you've got kind of like the animal brain, reptile brain cut list, fragment, is like the limbic system, basically. And you've got the cortex of the brain, purists will argue with this definition, but essentially, you've got the primitive brain and you've got the sort of smart brain where the brain is capable of planning and understanding concepts and different difficult things that a monkey can understand.

Now, the cortex is much, much smarter than your limbic system. Nonetheless, they work together well. I haven't met anyone who wants to delete their limbic system or the cortex, there are people quite happy having both. So you can think of this as being like the computer, the AI is like a third layer or a tertiary layer. So that is what could be symbiotic with the cortex, much smarter than the cortex. But you essentially have three layers. And you actually have that right now. Your phone is capable of things, and your computer is capable of things that your brain is definitely not, storing terabytes of information, perfectly, doing incredible calculations that we couldn't even come close to doing, you have that with your computer. It's just like I said, the data rate is slow, the connection is weak.

There is quite a bit of AI going on, new artificial neural nets. Increasingly, neural nets are sort of taking over from regular programming more and more. So you are connected, if you use Google Voice, or Alexa or one of those things, it's using a neural net to decode your speech and try to assign what you're saying. If you're trying to do image recognition, or improve the quality of a photograph, it's using the neural nets, the best way to do that. So, you are already sort of a cybernetic symbiote. It's like I said, just a question of your data rate. The communication speed between your phone and your brain is slow.

20 25 years from now, assuming civilization is still around, is looking fragile right now.

World Government Summit

(2017)

MAG = Mohammad Al Gergawi, Minister of Cabinet Affairs

EM = Elon Musk

MAG: We have seen within this part of the world great people like al-Khwarizmi who invented algorithm, globally: Newton, Henry Ford, The Wright brothers, Albert Einstein and Elon Musk.

I see you are in a rush, you want to go to places where nobody has been, you are reinventing a certain industry from the rocket industry with SpaceX to the car industry with Tesla. What's your mission in life? Why do you do whatever you do?

EM: And in terms of the motivations, I guess there is kind of a long version of the explanation. But essentially, when I was a kid, I was wondering kind of what's the meaning of life like, why are we here and what's it all about. I came to the conclusion that what really matters is trying to understand the right questions to ask. And the more that we can increase the scope and scale of human consciousness, the better we are able to ask these questions.

So, I think that there's certain things that are necessary to ensure that the future is good. And some of those things are in the long-term having long-term sustainable transport, and sustainable energy generation and to be a space-bearing civilization, and for humanity to be out there among the stars and be a multi-planetary species. I mean, I think being a multi-planet species and being out there among the stars is important for the long-term survival of humanity and that's one reason kind of like life insurance for life collectively- life as we know it. But then the part that I find personally most motivating is that it creates a sense of adventure, and it makes people excited about the future.

And if you consider two futures, one where we are forever confined to earth until eventually something terrible happens, or another future where we are out there on many planets maybe even going beyond the solar system. I think that the second version is incredibly exciting and inspiring and there need to be reasons to get up in the morning. Life can't just be about solving problems, otherwise what's the point. There's got to be things that people find inspiring and make life worth living.

MAG: So, what is life for you? I mean you look at our life and I heard you before speaking is the dream is that it is a Million D? What is life for Elon Musk?

EM: I find as I get older that question to be maybe more and more confusing or troubling or uncertain. I think particularly when you see the advancement of something like video games, you know like say 40 years ago you had video games, the most advanced video game would be like pong where you had like two rectangles and a dot like batting it back and forth.

MAG: I played it.

EM: We both played the same game and that was like “wow” that was a pretty fun game at the time. But now you can see a video game that's photorealistic, almost realistic and millions of people playing simultaneously. And you see where things are going with virtual reality and augmented reality. And if you extrapolate that out into the future with any rate of progress at all like even 0.1% or something like that a year, then eventually those games will be indistinguishable from reality. They'll be so realistic you will not be able to tell the difference between that game and reality as we know it. And then it seems like well how do we know that that didn't happen in the past and that we're not in one of those games ourselves.

MAG: Interesting.

EM: I mean could be.

MAG: Everything is possible in life.

EM: I mean, particularly like things seem to be accelerating to something.

MAG: Isn't it I mean if we look at our life, seems in the past 100 years life been accelerating fast, in the past 20 it's getting faster.

EM: It's getting faster and faster.

MAG: Is it slower. So, my question is really how life will be in 20, 30, 50 years from now, our education, our transport, how do you see it?

EM: Well, I think this is one of those things that's quite difficult to predict. I mean, the first controlled powered flight was 1903 with the Wright Brothers, and then 66 years later we put the first people on the moon. I mean, if you'd ask people in 1900 what the odds of a man landing on the moon, they would have said that's ridiculous. If you try to talk to them about the internet, they would not even know what the heck they are even talking about, like this sounds so crazy. But today with a hundred-dollar device you can video conference with anyone in the world, on the other side of the world. If you have a Wi-Fi connection you know, it's basically free; free to have an instant visual communication with anyone or even with millions of people. With social media you can communicate to millions of people simultaneously. So, you can google something and ask any question. It's like an article of wisdom that you can ask almost any question and get an instant response. It would have been incredibly difficult to predict these things in the past, even the relatively recent past.

So, I think the one thing that we can be quite certain of is that any predictions we make today for what the future will be like in 50 years will be wrong, that's for sure. I mean, I think directionally I can tell you what I hope the future has as opposed to maybe what it will be because this may just be wishful thinking. I mean, I hope we are out there on Mars and maybe beyond mars the moons of Jupiter. I hope we're traveling frequently throughout the solar system perhaps preparing for missions to nearby star systems. I think all of this is possible within 50 years, and I think that'll be very exciting to do that. I think we'll see autonomy and artificial intelligence advance tremendously. I think that's actually quite near term. My guess is in probably 10 years it will be very unusual for cars to be built that are not fully autonomous.

MAG: 10 years from now.

EM: Yes, I think almost all cars built will be capable of full autonomy in about 10 years. As it is, the Tesla cars that are made today have the sensor system necessary for full autonomy, and we think probably enough compute power to be safer than a person. So, it's mostly just a question of developing the software and uploading the software. And if it turns out that more compute power is needed, we can easily upgrade the computer. So, that's all Tesla's built since October of last year and other manufacturers will follow and do the same thing. So, getting in a car will be like getting in an elevator. You just tell it where you want to go and it takes you there with extreme levels of safety, and that'll be normal; it'll just be normal.

Elevators there used to be elevator operators. You get in maybe a guy moving a lever. Now you just get and you press the button and that's taken for granted. So, autonomy will be widespread.

I think one of the most troubling questions is artificial intelligence. I don't mean narrow AI; like a vehicle autonomy, I would put in the narrow AI class, it's narrowly trying to achieve a certain function. But deep artificial intelligence or what is sometimes called artificial general intelligence where you could have AI that is much smarter than the smartest human on earth. This I think is a dangerous situation.

MAG: Why is it dangerous? I mean, there are two views; one view is that artificial intelligence will help humanity; there is another school of thought that artificial intelligence is a threat to humanity. Why is it?

EM: Well, I think it's both. Imagine you're very confident that we were going to be visited by super intelligent aliens in let's say 10 years or 20 years at the most; super intelligent.

MAG: So, you think within 20 years we'll have alien on earth.

EM: Well digital super intelligence will be like an alien.

MAG: It will be like an alien.

EM: Yeah.

MAG: But my question is do you think there is other intelligent life outside the earth?

EM: It seems probable, but I think this is one of the great questions in physics and philosophy is where are the aliens? Maybe they're among us, I don't know. Some people think I'm an alien- not true.

MAG: Maybe we are Aliens Elon. I mean, if you look at this part of the world, they believe that human beings are not from earth; they came from somewhere else. Adam and Eve possibly came from somewhere else to earth. In a way, human beings are alien to this land. Do you think we will make contact with aliens within the next 50 years?

EM: Well, that's a really tough one to say. I mean, if there are super intelligent aliens out there, they're probably already observing us that would seem quite likely and we just are not smart enough to realize it. But I can do some back in the envelope calculations. Any advanced alien civilization that was at all interested in populating the galaxy, even without exceeding the speed of light, even if you're only moving at say 10 or 20% the speed of light, you could populate the entire galaxy in let's say 10 million years, maybe 20 million years max. This is nothing you know in the grand scheme of things.

MAG: Once you said you want to die on mars, why?

EM: To be clear, I don't want to die on mars. I mean, we're all going to die someday and if you're going to pick some place to die, then why not mars. If we're born on earth why not die on mars, it seems like maybe be kind of exciting. I think given the choice of dying on earth or dying on mars, I'd say yeah sure I'll die on mars, but it's not some kind of mars death wish. And if I do die on mars, I just don't want it to be on impact.

MAG: Okay got it. Let's come back to earth actually, you tweeted that you are building a tunnel under Washington, DC, why? What is it?

EM: Well, it's a secret plan just between us.

EM: Yes, please keep that secret. Well, it seems somewhat trivial or silly but I've been saying this for many years now, but I think that the solution to urban congestion is a network of tunnels under cities. I don't mean a 2d plane of tunnels. I mean, tunnels that go many levels deep. So, you can always go deeper than you can go up. The deepest mines are taller than the tallest buildings. So, you can have a network of tunnels that are 20_ 30_ 40_ 50 levels, if as many levels as you want really and so given that you can overcome the congestion situation in any city in the world.

The challenge is just figuring out how to build tunnels quickly and at low cost and with high safety. So, if tunneling technology can be improved to the point where you can build tunnels, fast, cheap and safe, then that would completely get rid of any traffic situations in cities. So, that's why I think it's an important technology. Washington, DC, LA and most of the major American cities most major cities in the world suffer from severe traffic issues. And it's mostly because you've got these tall buildings that are 3d, and you have a road network that is at one level. And then people generally want to go in and out of those buildings at the exact same time. So, then you get the traffic jam.

MAG: Let's come back to UAE and Dubai. The first time I met you it was 4th of June 2015 at your office in SpaceX. I ask you would you have a presence in the UAE and your answer was, “I'm busy with China, maybe, not in the near future.” And almost a year and a half later we are here. So, time goes quite fast. Why now?

EM: Well, I think actually things are going reasonably well in China. We had some initial challenges figuring out charging and service infrastructure and various other things. But now it's actually going fairly well, and so the timing seemed to be good to really make a significant debut in this region starting in Dubai.

MAG: Okay in your opinion what is the new disturbance thing that will come in technology. What is next, what's in technology?

EM: What's next in technology?

MAG: That will disturb the way we live, the way we think, the way we do business.

EM: Well, the most near-term impact from a technology standpoint is autonomous cars, like fully self-driving cars. Like I said that's going to happen much faster than people realize. It's going to be a great convenience to be an autonomous car but there are many people whose jobs it is to drive. In fact, I think it might be that the single largest employer of people is driving in various forms. So, then we need to figure out new roles for what those people do, but it will be very disruptive and very quick.

I should characterize what I mean by quick because quick means different things to different people. There are over two billion vehicles in the world, in fact, approaching two and a half billion cars and trucks in the world. The total new vehicle production capacity is about 100 million, which makes sense because the life of a car or truck before it's finally scrapped is about 20-25 years. So, the point at which we see full autonomy appear, will not be the point at which there is massive societal upheaval because it will take a long time to make enough autonomous vehicles to disrupt employment.

So, that disruption I'm talking about will take place over about 20 years. But still, 20 years is a short period of time to have I think something like 12 to 15 percent of the workforce be unemployed.

MAG: Thank you. This is the largest global government summit. We have over 139 governments here. If you want to advise government officials to be ready for the future, what are three things or advice you'll give them?

EM: Well, I think the first bit of advice would be to really pay close attention to the development of artificial intelligence. I think we need to just be very careful in how we adopt artificial intelligence and to make sure that researchers don't get carried away because sometimes what happens is a scientist can get so engrossed in their work, they don't necessarily realize the ramifications of what they're doing. So, I think it's important for public safety that the government keep a close eye on artificial intelligence and make sure that it does not represent a danger to the public.

Secondly, I would say, we do need to think about transport in general. There's the movement towards electric vehicles and sustainable transport. I think that's going to be good for many reasons but again, not something that happens immediately. That'll happen slower than self-driving vehicles. So, that's probably something that happens over 30 or 40 years after the transition to electric vehicles.

So, thinking about that in context, the demand for electricity will increase dramatically. So, currently in terms of total energy usage in the world, it's about one-third electricity about, one-third transport, about one-third heating. So, over time that will transition predominantly electricity; which means that the demand for electricity will probably triple. So, it's going to be very important to think about how you make so much more electricity.

MAG: It seemed they had an easy job. That's it. There are no more challenges for them.

EM: I think maybe these things do play into each other a little bit, but what to do about mass unemployment. This is going to be a massive social challenge. I think ultimately, we will have to have some kind of universal basic income. I don't think we're going to have a choice.

MAG: Universal basic income?

EM: Universal basic income, I think it's going to be necessary.

MAG: So, it means that unemployed people will be paid across the globe.

EM: Yeah.

MAG: Because there are no jobs. The machines and robots are taking over.

EM: There will be fewer and fewer jobs that a robot cannot do better. I want to be clear that these are not things that I think that I wish would happen. These are simply things that I think probably will happen. If my assessment is correct and they probably will happen then we need to say, what are we going to do about it. And I think some kind of a universal basic income is going to be necessary.

Now the output of goods and services will be extremely high. So, with automation. There will come abundance. Almost everything will get very cheap. So, I think the biggest thing we'll just end up doing is a universal basic income which is going to be necessary.

The harder challenge, much harder challenge is how do people then have meaning. A lot of people derive their meaning from their employment. If you're not needed, if there's not a need for your labor what's the meaning? Do you have meaning? Do you feel useless? That's a much harder problem to deal with. Then how do we ensure that the future is going to be the future that we want that we still like.

I do think that there's a potential path here which is and we're really getting into science fiction or sort of advanced science stuff. But having some sort of merger with biological intelligence and machine intelligence. To some degree we are already a cyborg. You think of the digital tools that you have, your phone, your computer, the applications that you have, like the fact that I was mentioning earlier you can ask a question and instantly get an answer from Google or other things. So, you already have a digital tertiary layer. I say tertiary because you can think of the limbic system kind of the animal brain or the primal brain and then the cortex kind of the thinking planning part of the brain and then your digital self as a third layer. So, you already have that. If somebody dies their digital ghost is still around, all of their emails and the pictures that they posted and the social media that still lives even if they died.

So, over time I think we'll probably see a closer merger of biological intelligence and digital intelligence. And it's mostly about the bandwidth the speed of the connection between your brain and the digital extension of yourself, particularly output. Output if anything is getting worse. We used to have keyboards that would use a lot- now we do most of our input through our thumbs on a phone, and that's just very slow. A computer can communicate at a trillion bits per second. But your thumb can maybe do 10 bits per second or 100 if you're being generous. So, some high bandwidth interface to the brain I think will be something that helps achieve a symbiosis between human and machine intelligence, and maybe solves the control problem and the usefulness problem.

MAG: It is close. We got it. You always think out of the box. Your ideas are so huge. You wanted to go to space, you did it. You decided that you want to land your rocket back, you failed 7 or 8 times, then landed.

EM: Yes, more times than I care to count.

MAG: How do you come with this idea? Sometimes they're pushing the human limit. You are always pushing the human limit?

EM: Well, I think about what technology solution is necessary in order to achieve the particular goal, and then try to make as much progress in that direction as possible. So, in the case of space flight the critical breakthrough that's necessary in space flight, is rapid and complete reusability of rockets just as we have for aircraft. You can imagine that if an aircraft was single-use almost no one would fly. Because you can buy like say a 747 might be 250 million dollars, 300 million or something like that you need two of them for a round trip. But nobody's going to pay millions of dollars per ticket to do air travel. But because you can reuse the aircraft tens of thousands of times, the air travel becomes much more affordable. And the same is true for rockets. So, our rocket costs 60 million roughly. So, the capital cost if it can be used once is 60 million dollars. But the capital cost if it can be used a thousand times is $60,000. So, then if you can carry a lot of people per flight, then you can get the cost of space flight to be something not far from the cost of air flight.

So, it's extremely fundamental. Because earth's gravity well is quite deep, earth has a fairly high gravity, the difficulty of making a rocket reusable is much greater than the difficulty of making an aircraft reusable; that's why a fully reusable rocket has never been developed thus far. But if you use the most advanced materials, most advanced design techniques and you get everything just right, then I'm confident that you can do a fully reusable rocket. Fortunately, if earth's gravity was 10% stronger, I'd say it would be impossible.

MAG: You need a team around you to deliver a lot of ideas. How do you choose your team? Based on what?

EM: Well, I suppose honestly that it tends to be a gut feel more than anything else. So, when I interview somebody, my interview question is always the same.

MAG: You ask?

EM: I say, "Tell me the story of your life and the decisions that you made along the way and why you made them. And also tell me about some of the most difficult problems you worked on and how you solved them." That question I think is very important because the people that really solve the problem, they know exactly how they solved it. They know the little details. And the people that pretended to solve the problem they can maybe go one level and then they get stuck.

MAG: So what was your biggest challenge in life?

EM: Biggest challenge in life? Well, there's a lot of them, which is the worst? I think just thinking about how to spend time. One of the biggest challenges, I think, is making sure you have corrective feedback loop, and then maintaining that corrective feedback loop over time, even when people want to tell you exactly what you want to hear, that's a very difficult.

MAG: I will ask you just one last question, sir. In the World Government Summit, we have so many people from across the globe. If you have an advice to the young people globally who want to be like Elon Musk, what's your advice to them?

EM: I think that probably, they shouldn't want to be me. I think it sounds better than it is. It's not as much fun being me as you think. I don't know.

MAG: You don't think so?

EM: But definitely it could be worse for sure. I'm not sure I want to be me. But for advice, if you want to make progress on things, I think that the best analytical framework for understanding the future is physics. I'd recommend studying the thinking process around physics, like not just not the equations. I mean, the equations certainly are helpful, but the way of thinking in physics is the best framework for understanding things that are counterintuitive.

And always taking the position that you are some degree wrong and your goal is to be less wrong over time. One of the biggest mistakes people generally make, and I'm guilty of it, too, is wishful thinking. You know, like you want something to be true, even if it isn't true. And so you ignore the real truth because of what you want to be true. This is a very difficult trap to avoid. And like I said, it's certainly one that I find myself having problems with. But if you just take that approach that you are always at to some degree wrong and your goal is to be less wrong and solicit critical feedback, particularly from friends.

If somebody loves you, they want the best for you. They don't want to tell you the bad things. So you have to ask them, I really do want to know and then they'll tell you.

MAG: Thank you very much. It is great for the World Government Summit to have a legend who's creating the future for humanity to share his thoughts, his idea, his vision, his challenges and his hope for life.

Axel Springer Award 2020

MD = Mathias Döpfner

EM = Elon Musk

Captain: Ladies and gentlemen, this is your captain speaking. Welcome aboard our vessel to Mars. Boarding is completed as all systems are set, and we're sure that we don't take the Coronavirus to outer space. Thanks for your cooperation by the way, we are ready to launch. First rule don't panic.

Announcer: Cabin crew prepare for takeoff.

20 seconds till take off. T-minus 15 seconds.

Eight, 7, 6, 5,4,3,2,1. Ignition lift off.

Captain: This is your captain with an update from the cockpit. We arrived in earth's orbit safe and sound. Let me please especially welcome one very special passenger. An extraordinary visionary multitalented engineer, a super smart entrepreneur, and not the least the man who made this mission to Mars possible. Please give a very warm welcome to Mr. Elon Musk. Please take a look at a wonderful planet. Isn't it gorgeous? As curious as I am to see Mars, I'm really looking forward to coming back to our old homestead.

Announcer: South Africa in the seventies, a boy from Pretoria facing childhood problems. He reads 10 hours a day: Star Wars and science fiction, but this one's got talent for machines and for money. At the age of 12, he programmed his first computer game on the good old commodore. Young Elon sold Blaststar for $500. Develop stuff, let it grow, sell it soon. This is how he made his fortune and his opportunity to go even further. This is the way. One sentence he never wanted to hear, you're in the army now. So he got himself a passport moved to Canada, leaving the South African apartheid regime behind, he was 16 years old. After some time in Kingston. He left Canada, went to Pennsylvania, got his bachelor and then moved south. Stanford University Palo Alto, where all the Silicon dreams were about to come true.

Elon was one of those who founded the legend of the Valley. With $2,000, a car and a computer and nothing more. He and his brother Kimball founded Zip2, a company that provided and licensed online city guide software to newspapers. Four years later, he sold it to Compaq for $307 million. Quite a story, but just the start. A typical story of those times, develop and invest. Find allies, merge, disrupt. The rise of PayPal. His first vision of making things easier for people using the digitization. Elon Musk helped to change the financial industry forever. PayPal was sold for $1.5 billion to E-Bay. Elon held 11.7% of the shares, a big winner in the big game. Money that he uses to make the world a better place.

He attacks on the world's best settled market, the automotive industry.

EM: We created Tesla to make a difference in the world.

Announcer: Tesla disruption at its best. Not everything worked out perfect, but his long breath proved him right. He is pushing all his competitors forward, he is expanding. He leads technology, he leads infrastructure and logistics. And if necessary, he works and sleeps at the factory.

EM: We've decided to put to the Tesla Gigafactory Europe in the Berlin area,

Announcer: And Tesla is just on the cutting edge of an idea. Autonomous driving is born.

EM: So for us being a little startup, we had to start off with a car that was in low production and necessarily expensive. But their idea of an electric car is something that doesn't look good and isn't fast, doesn't have high performance. We wanted to break the mold of all of that. That's what we sought to achieve.

Announcer: Saving time for important things, saving time for stuff that is fun. Well, it is fun to drive a Tesla, but on an endless motor way, even writing gets tiring. It's human, we're bored very soon. Let the car drive and get some food for the brain while it does the work. And last but not least fuel it with energy that is not harmful to the planet. Elon embraces his responsibility, but this is never enough, much more is needed. Elon can't stop thinking about the future of making things work better, more efficient. A visionary. A man who never gives up, although there would have been a few moments when giving up would have been a more than plausible option. He reaches out for the stars, the real ones. The stars shining bright at night in the sky.

EM: You see them both light up.

Announcer: And still the kid who loves sci-fi. Space X Is not only a business. It's not a hobby, it's a passion. Elon is CEO and its first spaceship designer. It is all rocket science really. Many laughed at him, NASA with its billions, the Russians with their ruthless and dead serious ambitions.

EM: The whole goal of Space X was for space exploration technology, and that's helping make humanity a space-faring civilization.

Announcer: He transported Americans to the ISS. Private economy is more effective and sustainable than state economy. Crew Dragon is a gentle slap in the face for over-the-top institutional rocketeers, the Russians took it personal, Elon Musk must not be quoted by them. Too successful. Russia, some things never change can one man change the world? Yes sure, Elon Musk did it and he doesn't stop there.

EM: And I think that's one of the things that makes people excited about the future. And we want the things that are in science fiction novels and movies, not to be science fiction forever. We want them to be real one day.

Announcer: What if one could help handicapped people by connecting the body with machines to reconnect neural disorders? Hey, presto! Neuralink. What. If we could get rid of traffic on our city streets, dig a deep long tunnel beneath them and shoot the cars from one side of the town to the other. Hey, presto! The Boring Company. The name by the way is one of the best puns ever. And stop, if we can do that with cars, why shouldn't we do it with goods and people in full speed, 600 kilometers in 35 minutes, just do it. Hey, presto! Hyperloop. But all that's earthbound, reach for the stars and planets. We're already on our way to Mars.

Captain: This is your captain speaking, well, rather gasping. What a trip that was! And it's not over yet. Let's hear it from the man himself. I'd kindly ask you now Elon to come on stage and join Axel Springer CEO Mathias Döpfner for a little chat.

EM: Well, that was fun.

MD: I'm glad that you enjoyed it.

EM: Yes, it's like a ride. I mean I think you could charge money for this. This was great. I mean yes it really makes a difference to have two screens and the angle change. That felt great like Disney ride.

MD: And apart from this special trip to Mars this evening, when do you think realistically human beings will land on Mars for the first time?

EM: I feel fairly confident about six years from now. So the Earth-Mars synchronization occurs roughly every 26 months. So we had one this year, the summer and so that means roughly like about two years, there'll be another one and then two years after that. So, I think I'd say if you say six years from now, I think highly confident, if we get lucky maybe four years. And then we want to try to send an uncrewed vehicle there in two years.

MD: When will your first trip to orbit will take place?

EM: I don't know, possibly in two or three years. I'm mostly concerned with developing the technology that can enable a lot of people to go to Mars and make life multi-planetary, have a base on the moon, a city on Mars. And I think it's important that we strive to have a self-sustaining city on Mars as soon as possible. I mean I'm optimistic about the future on earth, but it's important to have life insurance for life as a whole.

MD: Is it going to be a business kind of tourism in orbit? Or is it a more kind of plan B if things on Earth do not develop as well?

EM: It's not exactly a plan B. It's more, I think there's two aspects to this. One is that we want to have a future that is inspiring and exciting. And what are the things that you find inspiring and exciting about the future? I think one is a future where we are a space-faring civilization and out there among the stars. I think every kid gets excited about that, you don't even need to teach them, they just get it it's like instinctive. And so, it's very important for us to have reasons to be excited about life. Like when you wake up in the morning, it can't just be about problems.

I know everyone in this room deals with a lot of tough problems, but you know it's got to be more than that. So, you know I think a future where you can say, hey, even if it's not you, there's going to be people out there that are going, we're going to have a base on the moon. We're going to have a city on Mars, maybe go further moons of Jupiter and everything. I think that's a very exciting future and then I think most people do.

MD: And you seriously want to be buried on Mars?

EM: Just not an impact. Yes, I mean listen, we're all going to die someday. So, if you're going to die someday, I'm like, okay, do you want to be buried on Mars or Earth? I'm like Mars sounds cool, born on earth, die on Mars, that's if you've got the choice.

MD: Two years ago, I had a conversation with Jack Ma, and we spoke about Jeff Bezos's plans with regards to orbit and he said, well, let Jeff Bezos take care for the orbit, I take care for the earth. You seem to take care for both.

EM: Yes, basically Tesla is about trying to make sure things are good for the future on earth. And then Space X is about a good future beyond earth basically. And so obviously we have to have sustainable energy, both consumption and production of energy. So like Tesla does solar panels and batteries. I think that's one of the key, ways to have sustainable energy generation. And also the batteries are useful for wind power. So, and then you need to consume it via electric vehicles. I think I look at these things like say, okay and if you looked back from the future and say, what's the fundamental good of a Tesla? I would say it probably should be assessed as by how many years did Tesla accelerate the advent of sustainable energy? Like that's like I would measure the goodness of Tesla in that way. And then for Space X it's like okay, to what degree did we improve the probability of humanity being a space-faring civilization?

MD: I remember very well. The year, 2014, when we were hosting the Gold Steering Wheel here at Axel Springer, and you got the award for lifetime achievement. And I was sitting in the first row, with a then very successful and famous CEO of a very big German car company. And I asked him while you were on stage, isn't this guy dangerous for you? I mean this looks really serious. He said, oh no, don't worry. First of all, the whole idea of electric driving, it's never going to be a mass market.

EM: Sure, I've heard that a lot

MD: Second, these guys in Silicon Valley, they have no clue about engineering, about building really beautiful and great cars. So we don't have to worry. By then Tesla's market cap was 23 billion, today it's 536 billion US dollars. Market cap of VW then was 86 and today it's 77. And so you could, you are with Tesla two and a half times bigger than BMW, VW and Daimler.

EM: I even said the stock was too high. I mean, what am I supposed to do?

MD: Like have you ever considered that.

EM: The stock is too high a long time, like when it was $800 pre-pre-split. They didn't listen to me, but you know, I'll tell you and the SEC complained again, I mean like I know.

MD: Is it a serious option to buy one of the incumbents, one of the big car companies for you?

EM: Well, I think we're definitely not going to launch a hostile takeover. So I suppose if there was a lot.

MD: A friendly one.

EM: If somebody said, hey, we think it would be a good idea to merge with Tesla, we'd certainly have that conversation. But you know, we don't want to be a hostile takeover sort of situation.

MD: Did you feel a lot of complacency these days that the incumbents then let you feel that you are? I mean, the kind of hopeless disruptor but they know how to do it? Or were they very polite and nice with you.

EM: Do you mean back then or now?

MD: Back then.

EM: Oh, no.

MD: Today everybody's?

EM: They weren't super nice, I would not say they were. It was difficult to characterize their response as super nice. They used a lot of adjectives, I don't think any of them were positive. So, we really tried hard to convince a lot of companies. Honestly, I was in so many panels, generally the sentiment that was expressed that you mentioned earlier, that was pretty much universal. Especially back in say 2008 or 2007, like when we first unveiled the Roadster from 2007. Yes, I mean, it was just basically, they just said, well, you're basically a bunch of fools.

Well, I mean, generally they'd say like whoa! Starting a car company is crazy, you're going to lose all your money. I was like I think I probably will lose all my money, I agree. It wasn't like, I thought it would be successful. I thought we had maybe a 10% chance of success. So then people would say it's going to fail and you're going to lose, lose everything. I was like yes, probably true. Yes, what else is new.

MD: Couple of years ago, we saw each other in America and the guy asks you on a panel when autonomous driving will be approved. And you said, I do not care so much when it's going to be approved, I care more when human beings in cars will be forbidden. And then the guy said, well, that's totally unrealistic. It's never going to happen in cars. People want to do something actively. And then you said, well, a hundred years ago nobody could imagine an elevator without a lift-boy. Today, nobody could imagine a lift with a lift boy.

EM: Yes.

MD: So when is autonomous driving really going to happen? And when are you able to do it? And when is it going to be approved.

EM: Okay, just between us.

MD: Yes, that's a very discreet circle yes.

EM: So, well first of all, I'm not against people driving to be clear. So I think people will drive cars basically as far into the future, as I can imagine. It's just that it's going to be increasingly unusual to drive your own car. And while it's fun to drive a well-handling car on a winding road in beautiful terrain, of course, that's fun. But it's not fun to drive a car in terrible gridlock traffic, like going through extreme traffic, that's no fun driving a car. So, I think people are unlikely to most of the time, want to commute and drive themselves.

And people are typically spending an hour and a half a day, maybe two hours on average driving. Especially say like California or something like that it's very common. And some people will actually commute like three hours a day sometimes it's pretty crazy. So, I think if say fast forward to like 10 years from now, and then 10 years from now, almost all cars will have full autonomy capability, all new cars produced. So, there are about 2 billion cars and trucks in the existing fleet. And the new vehicle production is about 5% of the fleet size, so about a hundred million. So even the point at which all cars are autonomous, it will still take 20 years to replace all the cars, assuming that the number of cars and trucks in the fleet stays constant.

Like say 10 years from now, I would say vast majority of cars is electric, like maybe 70, 80% or more. And almost all cars autonomous: electric autonomy is absolutely the future no question. It's just a question of when. But then, like I said, as soon as people think that that means the global fleet gets replaced instantly. I was like, no, you have to go 20 years beyond that point, 20 years from the point at which all new cars are electric, then the fleet will be replaced. It is just as important to, it's not like so many people are used to mobile phones and that kind of thing is stuck two year or three-year replacement rate. But cars are much more expensive assets, longer life.

Anyway, to actually answer your question, I'm extremely confident of achieving full autonomy and releasing it to the Tesla customer base next year. Now there's an uncertain period of time for when regulatory approval will take. How long will it take? But I think if you are able to accumulate billions of kilometers of autonomous driving, then it's difficult to argue and look at the accident rate when the car is autonomous versus non-autonomous. And in fact, our statistics already show a massive difference when the car is on autopilot or not an autopilot. The safety is much greater, even with the current auto pilot's software.

MD: And we are discussing level 5 autonomy, so really.

EM: Yes.

MD: Full autonomy.

EM: Yes.

MD: Will Europe lag behind, or will it be approved here at the same time like in America or China?

EM: It's hard to say exactly when it will be approved, and our customers already know this. But the EU regulators are the most conservative, and I don't know if people want that to be the case or not, our customers are sort of unhappy about it. But, yes they only meet every six months, maybe meet more often I don't know. Yes, but I think at least some jurisdictions will allow full self-driving next year.

MD: Okay. Exactly a year ago you were announcing in this very building that you are planning to build a new site near Berlin.

EM: Yes.

MD: And a couple of months later in June, you started. You want to finish it by July next year. We did a little tour this morning. It's impressive how advanced it is and it's almost unbelievable. Germany and particularly Berlin is not world-famous for finishing construction sites in time and in budget.

EM: Yes.

MD: So you have created a kind of anti-Berlin airport project. Why Berlin? Why did you go to Germany and to Berlin to get that big project done?

EM: Sure. Well, first of all, I'm actually a big fan of Germany. I love Germany, it's great. I have a lot of friends, German friends and I think Berlin is a very fun city. And I think there's also from a location standpoint, like say young people can live in apartments at a reasonable price in the city of Berlin. But if someone's got a family, they can still have an affordable house. So, it's a good location offering a good living for people of all ages and incomes.

MD: Berlin mayor once said Berlin is poor but sexy. Is that what attracted you?

EM: Berlin it's not that poor, but it's definitely sexy. So we're going to have, when we open, you're all invited by the way. When we have the opening for Giga Berlin, we're going to have just a big party. We're going to have like start off on the day, have more sort of family music and then gradually get more hardcore and then go midnight Techno till Dawn.

MD: Do you plan to spend more time in Berlin yourself? You want to partly live here?

EM: In fact, yes. We spend a lot of time here.

MD: Where do you sleep tonight?

EM: Tonight's, it's in the factory.

MD: In the factory, not in a hotel?

EM: Technically in a conference room in the factory, but yes.

MD: You sleep in a conference room in the not finished factory tonight.

EM: Yes, it gives me a good feel for what's going on.

MD: Alone or?

EM: Yes, I assume so. Is this an invitation? Yes.

MD: Okay. Elon, you have so many projects: it's not only Tesla or Space X. It's Neuralink, it's The Boring Company. So many things that we discussed, last time I asked you what is the most important project or the most important topic for you to deal with in the foreseeable future. And you said that is truly the role that AI is going to play in our society. Could you explain why? And why that is a big opportunity that also seems to worry you.

EM: Well I mean, humans have been the smartest creature on earth for a long time, and that is going to change with what's typically called artificial general intelligence. So this is say an AI that is a smarter than a human in every way could even simulate a human. This is something we should be concerned about. I think there should be government oversight of AI development, especially super advanced AI. Anything that is a potential danger to the public, we generally agree that this should have a government oversight to ensure that the public safety is taken care of.

MD: Because you feel that one day that mankind could serve the machines and not the other way around?

EM: Honestly, when I see people on their phones, I think we already serving the machine.

MD: It's happening now.

EM: It's like everyone answering the questions. You know, every time you do a search or add information, you're sort of building the digital group mind. But yes, the advent of artificial general intelligence is called the singularity for a reason, because just like a black hole, which is a single error singularity, it's difficult to predict what will happen. So it's not as though the advent of AGI is necessarily bad, but it's bad as one of the possible outcomes.

MD: And when is the singularity as in the definition of Ray Kurzweil going to happen?

EM: I think he's predicting 2025. I think that's reasonably accurate.

MD: And how can it be avoided? that is then more a threat for humanity than an opportunity. Is it a question of governance so that there is not too much power in one or in few hands. Or how would you make sure that it goes into the right direction?

EM: I think we should have a government oversight just like we have government oversight and regulation of cars and aircraft and food and pharmaceuticals. There are regulators that oversee, these developments to ensure public safety, and I think a digital superintelligence would also be potentially a public safety risk. I think it's very important for regulators to keep an eye on that.

MD: Who should own the data by then?

EM: I think everyone should own their own data, like individuals who own their data. And it certainly shouldn't be tricked by some terms and conditions of a website and suddenly you don't own your data that's crazy. Who reads those terms and conditions anyway? But I think it's just, we wouldn't let people develop a nuclear bomb in the backyard just for the hell of it you know, that seems crazy. So digital superintelligence I think has the potential to be more dangerous than a nuclear bomb. Somebody should be keeping an eye, we can't have the inmates running the asylum here.

MD: Which is a global issue, because if we do well, but China has other rules and a different regulatory framework. that is another challenge.

EM: This is one of the rebuttals I get from those developing AI, Tesla is also developing a form of AI with self-driving, but it's a very narrow form of AI. Like the car is not going to wake up one day and take over the world. But the rebuttal, I get is well, you know, China is going to have unfettered AI development and so if we have regulations and that slows us down, then China will have it. And I'm like, look from my conversations with government officials in China, they're quite concerned about AI as well. And the fact that they're probably more likely to have a good oversight than I think other countries.

MD: What is the biggest challenge ahead of us? In general, not only with regard to AI. What is the biggest problem that needs to be solved?

EM: What's the biggest threat to humanity's future or something? Well, AI is certainly one of the biggest risks, it could be the biggest risk. I think we need to watch out about population collapse: this is somewhat counterintuitive to most people. They think that well, there are so many humans, maybe too many humans, but that's just because they live in a city. If you're an aircraft and you look down and say, if you dropped a cannonball, how often would you hit a person? Basically, never. In fact, there are staff falling in from space all the time: natural meteorites, all rocket stages all the time. But nobody worries about it because the actual, in fact, there's a cool website called Wait, but Why? And Scott Timmerman, like he actually just did the math and all humans on earth could fit in the city of New York on one floor. Don't even need the upper floors.

So that's actually the cross-section of humans as seen from earth is extremely tiny, basically vanishingly small, almost nothing. So we need to watch out about population collapse, low birth rate I think is a big risk. And it's also not exactly top secret, you can go and look at the Wikipedia, you know birth rate. So, and this is definitely the civilization ends with a whimper not a bang, because it would be a sad ending, where the average age becomes very high and really the youth are effectively de facto enslaved to take care of the old people. This is not a good way to end.

MD: Do you have any new projects dealing with this, the topics that you've just addressed?

EM: Well, I'm trying to set a good example on the kid front.

MD: Six kids.

EM: Yes, for now,

MD: How much time do you spend with them?

EM: I spend about as much time as they want to spend with me. I mean they're not, well, one's just a baby and now there's

14 and 16 and teenagers, don't usually want to hang out with their parents that much, you know. You know, we just had the Thanksgiving weekend, so all the kids were over, but if they want to spend more time with me, I actually asked them are you sure you even want to hang out more? Like, no. So, I think it's probably the right amount then since they don't want to hang out more.

So I think we really should take this seriously, the population collapse, artificial intelligence, obviously sustainable energy is important. The faster we transition to sustainable energy, the less of a gamble we're taking with climate. And I think there's going to be a lot of breakthroughs on the medical front, particularly around synthetic mRNA. All that you can basically do anything with the synthetic RNA DNA. It's like a computer program, so, I mean I think with enough effort that's not too crazy, you could probably stop aging, reverse it if you want. You can transform someone into a freaking butterfly if you want, with the right DNA sequence. So my caterpillars do it.

MD: But you have project Neuralink is in a way empowering human intelligence versus artificial intelligence. That's the purpose of it? Is that correct?

EM: In the short to medium term Neuralink is really just going to, help cure brain injuries, the brain and spine injuries. So it's like if somebody is, in fact, our first implanted devices in humans will be for quadriplegics, tetraplegics allowing them to control a computer or a phone, just using the mind. You can imagine like if Stephen Hawking could just talk at normal speed or even faster than normal speed.

MD: Looking back for the last thousands of years, what is the most important invention of mankind so far?

EM: The past thousand years? I guess it's

MD: Millions.

EM: Oh millions. Well, I think language being able to talk and express concepts and this is probably the, the biggest invention of humanity is language.

MD: It's an answer that we like very much in a publishing house.

EM: Yes, absolutely. Writing is exactly, just incredible. Writing really made a big difference. That guy, Gutenberg, he really knows what he's doing.

MD: You have one thing in common with Nicholas Tesla, that's a photographic memory. Is that only a gift or sometimes a burden because you memorize too much?

EM: I have a photographic memory in some respects.

MD: Censor?

EM: For technical stuff, I have a very good memory, for a human. Yes, computers are much better at memory computers are really good at memory.

MD: Why is music so important for you, techno music in particular?

EM: Well, it's pretty fun. You want to feel maximum human, you know? And so I think when people have like sort of a rave and good music, it can be like, hey, maximum human. You want to really feel, it's like what really gets you to feel, you know? And I think that having fun with friends and, just crazy dancing is fun.

MD: Perhaps your love for techno music is the secret reason why you are building big projects in Berlin.

EM: Honestly, that's a significant factor.

MD: Okay Elon, last question. You celebrated your 30th birthday with a masked ball in Venice.

EM: 40th.

MD: For your 40th birthday, I was told you had a fight with a samurai sword fighter. What is your plan for your 50th birthday next year?

EM: So my 40th birthday was in Venice; it was technically a post-apocalyptic masked ball. Cause you know after the apocalypse, how much clothes do you really have? I got to be a little ragged, a little burnt.

MD: So, no plans for the 50th?

EM: Yes 50th, the half-century party. I'll have to think of something, usually go with some kind of crazy theme. But the party where I ended up wrestling with world champion sumo wrestler, which by the way, also caused me to burst a disc in my neck. So you have five minutes of glory for five years of pain, it was really hard. So that party was Victorian Japanese steam punk, so that was cool. I have to think of something for a half-century party.

MD: You have a little time to think about.

EM: Hey, being on earth for a half-century, that's like, hey, I'm still alive. Wow. Cool.

MD: Okay Elon, one very last question. When I asked you, what is the meaning of life during a dinner.

EM: 42.

MD: You said after a while well, probably this wonderful French cheese. Could you please explain?

EM: Well, I was just saying that you want to take a moment to appreciate things in life and the sensations. Food's incredible and there's just so many good things that you can experience, some of them cost nothing really. You know have a walk-in nature or just a nice meal and it's like, wow, it was pretty great you know. And we should take a moment to appreciate these little things, the big things, the things that move your heart. I think that's probably the meaning of life as close a definition is, as I can think.

MD: Thank you very much Elon.

EM: All right.

Captain: This is your captain speaking again. Thank you Elon. Thank you, Mathias. It's a pleasure having you on board and learning so much about our future. Before I come back with some information about our flight, I'm now honored to welcome Secretary Jens Spahn and ask him onstage and to share his thoughts about Elon Musk's achievements and responsibilities.

Mr. Musk, I'm pleased to have the honor of paying tribute to you in this very special time. You are without doubt a visionary. The name Musk stands for ideas that were often far ahead of their time.

Paying online with PayPal, electromobility and sustainable energy with Tesla. And not seldom does the name Musk also represent ideas that at first glance might seem a little crazy. The Hyperloop project is one of those, the vision that persons and goods can be accelerated in the double tube to speeds of up to 1200 kilometers per hour. This also includes connecting the human brain to a computer, the subject of Neuralink just discussed Neuralink's research since 2016. And of course, private space travel with Space X is also an integral part of the mission. Thanks to Elon Musk, seemingly crazy ideas become reality. Elon Musk has realized the most powerful thing we as human beings possess is our ideas.

Tesla's ability to rise, to become the world's most valuable car manufacturer was not primarily the result of its sales figures, Tesla's worth is a reflection of an idea, a vision. An idea that allows many people to have faith in progress, in a better future. It is supported, of course, by business expertise. Elon Musk is building his newest Gigafactory in Brandenburg on Mark land. Many Germans associate Brandenburg with the poet Theodore Fontane, who once walked the sense of the Mark Fontane wrote, between arrogance and humility lies the third trait that is part of life and that's simply put, is courage. Should you not yet know Fontane by the way, for your Douglas Adam non-digital bookshelf, I hope there is one Fontane. Should you not yet know him, Mr. Musk? I think that fits you quite well, because courage you most certainly have.

At the same time, your choice of Germany as the location for your factory is hardly only a question of courage, but just as much the result of keen calculation. Germany is a country of automobile pioneers: Karl and Bertha Benz, Rudolf Diesel, Gottlieb Daimler, Ferdinand Porsche. The list of achievements by Germans are made in Germany is long. Mr. Musk, you know that Germany still possesses great innovative strength today. Many well-trained creative people and a solid infrastructure.

Great conditions for courageous entrepreneurship, for tomorrow's innovators and pioneers.

Indeed, constructing a factory from scratch and only in a few months, that is a new experience even for our country or at least an experience we seem to have forgotten. We need a bit more of the Musk courage on our side to reduce bureaucratic obstacles and thereby promote innovation. Because also it is true that innovation needs a reliable framework, it also needs freedom to flourish. In the 70 years since the creation of the Federal Republic of Germany, we have often succeeded in striking this balance. Germany is an economically strong country, cosmopolitan and free. An anchor of stability and amity in Europe, it is something we can be proud of. Today, however, at the start of the twenties of the 21st century, there are a number of questions we also ask ourselves. What do we want the twenties to look like? How can we find the right answers in complicated times?

What legacy do we want to leave to our children? How can we maintain the German success model, sustain and expand our prosperity as well as the freedom and security associated with it in times where it is under threat from many sides? So we need a strong state that encourage economic activity, because German firms can't. Because German firms suffer some clear disadvantages when competing with monopolies from the US and with a state economy like China's. In return, our state should invest massively in education, infrastructure, and research, and should launch support programs, not for individual companies, but for entire branches of the economy. In the twenties, we want to remain expert champion, a master of innovation, push forward digitalization, promote research and strengthen an entrepreneur culture. Only progress will ensure that the next generation will have it even better.

It's all about making space for ideas to flourish. From all that we've heard, Elon Musk knows this and tries to implement it in his businesses. Being a visionary does not necessarily mean always being right, nor does it mean being free of contradiction. It was only recently that Elon Musk and I got to meet each other personally and we're also able to talk about the pandemic situation. Tesla through the subsidiary, Groment Automation, a partner of the German Dutch biotech company Kubik, which is doing research on a Corona virus vaccine. Kubik is using RNA bioreactors developed by Elon Musk companies. I'm very pleased to see this commitment, however, I have read that Elon Musk himself does not intend to get vaccinated. I also note that Elon Musk takes a critical view of many of the measures that we, as governments are taking to control the pandemic and to protect our citizens.

One of his statements struck me, especially that anyone who is at risk should be in quarantine until the storm passes. In connection with the observation, you just made again tonight that everyone has to die sometime. Yes house protection does not take precedence over all else. In the pandemic it is always about balance. No matter how we act or do not act, harm will occur. We must therefore strike a balance. As Minister of

Health. I think it is only right for us to weigh health protection very highly. I for one would have great difficulty doing otherwise. At the same time, it is legitimate to demand a different rating, such debates are an indispensable part of our free societies. And it is important that we are not implacable in these discussions. But we listen to each other and are willing to assume at least sometimes that the other one might have a point or that their arguments could be valid. Debates that deteriorate into moralizing, seldom reflect reality in all its diversity.

So it would be highly unfair to imply that Elon Musk might care too little. Through his private foundation Elon Musk funds research into renewable energy, space travel, child health, education, and mathematics, computer science, natural science technology, as well as safe AI. In his private capacity, he is consistently donating large sums of money to charity projects such as for planting 1 million trees. Looking at Elon Musk means repeatedly encountering a seemingly insatiable zest for action and discovery. The many articles about the supposedly declining, innovative power of our Western world and societies then just seems to be worlds away. In such instances, Elon Musk stands in the limelight. He is the spearhead of an entire generation of courageous entrepreneurs and both scientists. People who believe in the power of ideas and that progress is possible in spite of resistance and setbacks. This gives us courage, despite the great challenges that we as humans are currently facing, we are living in a time of great opportunity. An economically successful, environmentally responsible and socially balanced world is possible. It is possible through innovation and courage, not through individual austerity or through fear. Experiences and encounters with innovative and creative people such as Elon Musk reconfirm my basic optimism time after time: we do have the power to shape our future. Elon Musk wanted to change the world a little and ended up revolutionizing it. This teaches us that everything is in our own heads, it is up to each and every one of us. Above all now in this often difficult time, we may not lose sight of the future ahead of us. With all of its alarming disastrous aspects in many areas, the current pandemic strengthens precisely the willingness to shape the future.

It is leading us faster than ever down some appropriate and necessary path. As the old saying goes, crisis presents opportunity. And this pandemic, we are learning more on a daily base together, in other words, in public. We are adapting our strategies, we are consistently trying to act in a targeted and proportionate way, starting afresh every day, based on the latest knowledge. This spirit of progress, this openness, willingness to learn is something we must sustain in the future. I'm convinced that Germany has a great deal of this visionary power that drives you Mr. Musk. We simply need to more often have the courage to believe in it ourselves. In this respect, you are a great example to us. Congratulations on the 2020 Axel Springer Award. I wish you the greatest possible success for the future and even more stay healthy. All the best

Interview with Mathias Döpfner, CEO of Axel Springer

(2020)

MD = Mathias Döpfner

EM = Elon Musk

MD: Wolfgang Schäuble, a wise German politician, said: "If there is an absolute value in our Basic Law at all, then it is the dignity of man. That is inviolable. But it does not exclude that we must die."

EM: Everyone dies.

MD: Everyone dies. But dignity is something that should be protected. Even in times of corona. Did you change any of your views with regard to the virus during your own infection?

EM: No, honestly.

MD: What is your outlook, let's say, for the summer of next year. Will the vaccination do its work?

EM: We're going to have so many vaccines, we will not know what to do with them. More vaccines than we can possibly use.

MD: But with a positive side effect on cancer medication.

EM: If you say, what are the silver linings of vaccine production, then the vaccine technology got turbocharged, that's for sure. There is a massive interest in the acceleration of vaccines. The mRNA vaccines in particular are very interesting because they can be potential cures for cancer. I think the work of BioNTech, CureVac, Moderna — the future of medicine is mRNA. You can cure basically anything with mRNA. It is just like a computer program, basically a synthetic virus. You can program it to do anything you want. You could turn into a butterfly practically.

MD: So, it will be a huge boost for the economy.

EM: It's a lot of money that's flowing to them. We're also much better with testing. Testing technology has improved dramatically.

MD: You were given a lifetime award as part of the Golden Steering Wheel in Berlin in 2014. I was sitting next to a very famous CEO of a very big German car company. When you were onstage, I asked him: "Aren't you worried by this guy? I mean, what he's doing is really serious." He said: "No, no, I don't worry. Absolutely not. He may have this crazy idea about battery cars, but that's not going to be a mass-market thing. And secondly, these guys just don't know how to build nice cars. They don't have the engineering expertise."

EM: That's interesting. We needed to improve for sure.

MD: What do you think about this complacency?

EM: Complacency is never wise.

MD: He was absolutely serious. "This is never going to work." And now Tesla, which is worth $536 billion today, is 2 1/2 times bigger than VW, Daimler, and BMW together. Herbert Diess said, half-jokingly, Tesla actually could take over VW. Would that be attractive to you at all?

EM: Our approach is probably going to be to execute independently. But we can either manufacture or license some of our technology to companies like BMW. We're trying to be as pure as possible here with respect to our goal, which is to accelerate the advent of sustainable energy. So, it's not about creating competitive walled gardens or anything like that. We're going to be making our Supercharger network available to other companies; we're going to offer licensing of Autopilot. They want to use our autonomy. And we can potentially do something with battery cells. And, you know, we're willing to license technology to help other companies do the right thing.

MD: Traditional takeovers are not a strategy for Tesla?

EM: Traditional takeovers are tough because companies have their own culture. Maybe if a company said to us, "Please, we're interested in merging with Tesla," that would be considered. But we wouldn't want to launch a hostile takeover. We would consider it ourselves if they approached us and said they're interested in merging companies.

MD: Did you feel the complacency of the incumbents six years ago?

EM: The incumbents were quite arrogant. Their words were not kind words.

MD: Were they literally aggressive in a way?

EM: Oh yeah.

MD: Did it harm Tesla at all? Or did it help because it motivated you and your people?

EM: We didn't take it too personally. But generally, when there's some new technology in an industry, that is how the incumbents react. It's natural. For us it was in the end a big motivation. At some point we did try to do some kind of joint ventures with Daimler and Toyota. However, we found that the enthusiasm of our partners was not big enough. So, we ended up winding down those partnerships and just stuck to building our own cars. I think that has changed a lot.

MD: What changed exactly?

EM: It's now clear that people want electric cars. They want sustainable transport. They want clean energy. This really tends to be somewhat of an age-related attitude. The younger somebody is, the more they care about the environment. And so, as time goes by, they grow older, and then they become the decision-makers. That's the normal way of the world.

MD: How many units do you want to sell with Tesla in 10 years?

EM: There are about 2 billion cars and trucks active in the world, and that number is increasing. Internally we think, we would like to be changing 1% of the fleet in the global fleet per year. To really make a dent, we have got to be past the decimal point. So that would be about 20 million vehicles a year.

MD: Which means that the current valuation is kind of justified. You made a comment and said it's too high. Why did you do that?

EM: Actually, it was when it was much lower than it currently is. I said that when it was around $800 a share, and that was before the split. We had a five-point split. The stock market is a strange thing. It's like having a manic depressive who's constantly telling you how much your company's worth. And sometimes they have a good day, and sometimes they have a bad day, but the company is basically the same. The public markets are crazy. So, do I think there's a good chance that Tesla's worth this in the future? Yes, possibly more. But it really depends on the probability that people think we will actually get to 20 million vehicles a year. And then also solar and stationary battery storage are a very important part of Tesla's future.

MD: Do your incumbents have a fair chance at playing a role in the kind of competitive ecosystem, or is it too late for them?

EM: It's definitely not too late. We are seeing a significant movement towards electrification from VW. And a lot of the Chinese companies are very, very, very fast. I would guess the most competitive company for Tesla might be a company that was created in China. The market there is extremely competitive. They have some very good companies, and they work super hard. But at this point, all the major car companies, if not 80%, then 90%, have said they're moving quickly towards electrification.

MD: So, you are bullish, remain bullish on electrification. Has anything changed with regard to self-driving? I remember, a couple of years ago, you were asked when do you think there will be permission for self-driving cars. And you said: "I don't care about the moment when self-driving will be permitted. I care about the moment when it will be forbidden for human beings to drive a car." And then somebody said, this is never going to happen, because nobody can imagine sitting in a car without steering it. And then you said, "Well, nobody could imagine a hundred years ago that an elevator would be possible without a lift boy. Today, you cannot imagine a lift with a lift boy." Do you still believe in that analogy?

EM: I want to be clear. I'm definitely not trying to take anyone's steering wheel away from them. I'm just saying what will most likely occur, and I am certain about this, is that self-driving will become much safer than a human driver. Probably by a factor of 10. This means that the standard for allowing someone to drive their own car is probably going to become higher. Currently, getting a driver's license is relatively easy, because people need a car to get around. But often they crash their car, for various reasons, because they are drunk or distracted. Or there's a lot of texting while driving. So, the standard for being able to drive your own car in the future when autonomy is 10 times safer than human driving will become much more stringent. That's the most likely outcome.

MD: And what is the time horizon — when will level-five autonomy happen? And do you believe that level four is ever going to be executed? Because then you have a combination of humans and machines, which can be more dangerous than machines only.

EM: There is a dangerous transition point. Where self-driving is good, but it occasionally has issues, because people maybe get too comfortable, and then they stop paying attention like they should. And then 99.9% of the time, it's good, 1 in 1,000 times it's not. And you really need more like six nines, like a 99.9999 sort of reliability.

MD: But any prediction about by when it will be the new normal?

EM: I'm extremely confident that Tesla will have level five next year, extremely confident, 100%.

MD: You will be able to provide that, but what about when it is going to be approved?

EM: I don't control the timeline for approval.

MD: But Tesla could do it next year in theory?

EM: Absolutely. I drive the alpha build of the latest, fully self-driving software for Tesla, and many times I can go through a very complicated series of intersections and narrow roads, without ever touching any of the controls. All the way to work and back.

MD: And approval, any prediction for that in the US, in Europe, in China?

EM: In the US, it will be pretty quick to approve, particularly in certain states. Some countries, like perhaps Norway, will be very quick to approve. They've said that. The EU is where we actually have the most difficulty. It's quite challenging. And the committee only meets every six months, and then the agenda is decided six months before that. So, it's very difficult. Our biggest challenges for regulatory approval are in the EU. This is a case of too many cooks in the kitchen, maybe.

MD: You're also making great progress with batteries, in terms of durability. There is one thing that you need for your product, and that is commodities. You mainly need lithium, you need copper, you need cobalt.

EM: Actually, nickel is our biggest constraint.

MD: These things are relatively scarce, they come from countries, most of which are not democratic. Some of these goods are mined using child labor and other terrible things. So, isn't this an issue that worries you? On the one hand you're thinking about finding a solution that will contribute to the well-being of the planet and the climate. But the side effect may be that totalitarian regimes are strengthened, or people have to work in terrible conditions.

EM: We actually publish a sort of sustainability report. We insist, for all of our suppliers, that the materials are ethically sourced. And this is verified with the party organizations. So, I'm highly confident that no child labor is being used for any of our mining operations. If there is, and somebody can point that out, we will take immediate action. Besides that, cobalt is a very important economic resource for the Congo. People are really counting on this money.

MD: Apart from the ethical question, are you not worried that this could just create a scarcity that could one day be a limiting factor, and you might simply not have enough of the material at some point?

EM: I'm confident that, within the Earth's crust, there's plenty of material for electric vehicles. This is not going to be a fundamental constraint.

MD: Grünheide, I was there this morning, and it's amazing. I remember November last year, when you announced the project at an Axel Springer event in this room. The construction got started in June this year, and in July next year it is going to be finished. Twelve thousand people in the first step, 40,000, potentially, if the whole compound is totally developed. I think your budget was 1.1 billion. Do you think you're going to finish it within budget? And in time?

EM: Unfortunately, we will exceed the budget. This is the nature of things.

MD: Just to compare: The little concert hall in Hamburg called the Elbphilharmonie was originally budgeted at 77 million, it was finished 10 years later for 866 million. Berlin's new airport was supposed to be finished in 2011 but has only just been opened. Its original budget was 1.7 billion, it finished at 7.3 billion.

EM: Wow! Well, I sure hope that doesn't happen with us.

MD: What you're doing here is a kind of standing provocation for prestigious real-estate-development projects in Germany — they tend to run out of budget, do not meet the original planned time frame. What is the secret behind your speed? Are you personally so involved?

EM: I'm personally very involved. Right now, I'm spending more time on the Giga Berlin than any other thing at Tesla.

And actually, I'm spending a lot of time on just working through the permits.

MD: You still don't have a permit? You just started with a temporary permit.

EM: Yeah, technically we have a temporary permit. So, it's a risk. But hopefully we will get the permanent permit soon. We have a good relationship with the permit office — they are working very hard. I do think that, at a high level, someone has to review the rules and regulations in Germany. Actually, it would be very important from a policy standpoint to have a rule-removal committee or some organization, some entity that reexamines the rules to say these no longer apply, these should be changed. Something like that would be really helpful for the whole country.

MD: When you talk to politicians and regulators, do you have the impression that they're seriously considering that?

EM: The regulators themselves are the ones pressing for the permits, and they're simply executing the rules that they have been given. So, it needs to be at a high level, I think at a political level. Some of these rules are like somebody made them maybe 20, 30, 40 years ago. Maybe they're still good, maybe they're not. And if no one's looking at them, then every year we just get more rules and regulations and laws. And eventually you won't be able to do anything.

MD: You know it is a kind of European issue in particular, perhaps a German issue. Nevertheless, you decided to go to Germany and to build near Berlin. Was that also motivated a bit by this idea, I'm going to the country of the incumbents of the global automotive industry and go right where they are? Or was it purely driven by access to talent, the fact that it's a great and cheap place?

EM: First of all, it was important for Tesla to have a significant production and engineering presence in Europe. So, you know, it doesn't make sense from an efficiency standpoint to build cars in California and ship them halfway around the world.

MD: Purely for logistical reasons?

EM: It's also not good for the environment to be transporting cars for such a long distance. So, for efficiency and environmental reasons, it makes sense to build the cars where the customers are reasonably close. And then obviously, we need one in Europe. You at least want to have a factory there, and I think it's also about engineering and design. And I guess I also had a personal preference for the Greater Berlin area, because Berlin's a lot of fun. And there's a lot of talent in Germany, for sure. A lot of my good friends are German. I like going to Berlin.

MD: So hedonistic motives played a role?

EM: I've got to go somewhere. And, obviously, Munich would be a good choice, but that's kind of BMW's home territory: Bavarian Motor Works, so that sounds OK. But we're up here, basically in Prussia, and I'm a big fan of history. And I like Frederick the Great, and he really was great and anyone who studies history knows he was great.

MD: One hundred years ago, Berlin was the power hub of the creativity business and value creation. And nightlife. Do you want to re-create that?

EM: Yeah, Berlin has the best night clubs.

MD: We'll come back to that topic later. Could you imagine living here personally?

EM: Well, I've set out to be a bit of a gypsy or something. I will definitely be spending quite a lot of time in Berlin, yeah.

MD: Are you looking for places?

EM: No, I'm not really buying any places. I stay at a hotel sometimes.

MD: Where are you sleeping tonight?

EM: I'm just going to be sleeping at the factory in one of the conference rooms.

MD: You'll be sleeping in a conference room in the factory?

EM: Yeah.

MD: Alone?

EM: That's my understanding, yeah. You've got to get a feel for the situation.

MD: You said, in a recent quote, that possession just weighs you down. And that's why you want to get rid of your possessions. And that's why you have literally started to sell property. You have sold belongings. Is it more a metaphor or are you literally selling your belongings?

EM: I sold my primary home.

MD: The one in LA?

EM: It was done two months ago. It was actually bought by a guy in China. And then I sold the house I own across the road, which used to be owned by Gene Wilder. It's very much his personality, and I sold it below market to his nephew who grew up there. And then we're in the process of selling my other houses. I guess I'll rent a place somewhere.

MD: So why are you doing it? Because it's too much of an obligation, or it's limiting your freedom? You are considered to be the second-wealthiest person in the world. And now you are getting rid of your property.

EM: In fact, I'll have basically almost no possessions with a monetary value, apart from the stock in the companies. So, if things are intense at work, I like just sleeping in the factory or the office. And I obviously need a place if my kids are there. So, I'll just rent a place or something. And a lot of the time it's just me, so I don't really need a big place.

MD: So, no art collection, no cars, no real-estate property, no other stuff that we usually associate with wealthy people. Do you believe that getting rid of all that makes you a free man?

EM: Yes, essentially, I think that also. Like the reason that I am accumulating wealth, if you will, which is really just stock in Tesla and SpaceX. The only publicly traded stock I own is Tesla. That's it. If Tesla and SpaceX go bankrupt, I will go bankrupt personally. One-hundred percent. But I also think, why should I try to have stock anyway. Why do I have all this stuff? Going back to what I was saying earlier, I think it is important for humanity to become a spacefaring civilization and a multiplanet species. And it's going to take a lot of resources to build a city on Mars. I want to be able to contribute as much as possible to the city on Mars. That means just a lot of capital.

MD: And you want to focus on that?

EM: Yes, and I'm also just trying to make clear that I'm serious about this. And it's not about personal consumption. Because people will attack me and say, oh, he's got all these possessions. He's got all these houses. OK, now I don't have them anymore.

MD: There is one priority you said may also limit your freedom but nevertheless seems to be a top priority for you, and those are your kids. You have six.

EM: For the moment that's correct.

MD: Could you explain why kids are so incredibly valuable for you? And why you are defending or encouraging people wherever you can to give birth to kids?

EM: Absolutely. My friends all say, oh, man, there it goes with the kids again, saying we should have kids and so on. But a lot of my friends have no kids. No, maybe they have one. And I'm like, man, how are we going to keep humanity going if you don't have kids? A lot of countries have a negative replacement rate. You can't just solve it with immigration — that's not possible. So, if you believe in humanity at all, you've got to say, we need to make sure we have humans in the future. They don't come from nowhere.

A lot of people would say they have the impression that the Earth is overpopulated. This is totally false. And they're just basing this on their immediate impressions because they live in a dense city. Have you gone to the countryside or looked down from an airplane? What percentage of the time, if you dropped a cannonball, would it drop on somebody? Basically zero percent.

MD: A friend of mine, who had a very unhappy childhood, came to the conclusion not to give birth to any kids. Your childhood was also not the happiest one. Nevertheless, you are drawing the opposite conclusion, wanting to have as many kids as possible.

EM: I'm not sure it's as many as possible — I can technically have a lot more. But yeah, I like kids. I'm trying to set a good example.

MD: Is it true that you were bullied at school?

EM: I had a very unhappy childhood. There were many years when I was very sad.

MD: What was the reason?

EM: It was hell at school and hell at home.

MD: In school, because your peers realized that you are a different breed, and therefore bullied you, or how do you explain that?

EM: It's important to know that South Africa is a very, very violent place. Violence is normal. And it's not unusual, so I'm not talking about just words.

MD: Physical violence?

EM: I was almost beaten to death at one point. So, it was a close call. I was in hospital for a while. So anyway, this is not a rare story, frankly.

MD: Do you think that motivated you to play a pivotal role in improving the world? Was it in a way, like the kind of traumas we experience in our childhood are very often the motivators for excellence and achievements in our lives?

EM: I was a pretty motivated kid. Even when I was very young, so I think it could have increased my motivation. But the thing that helped the most was that I just read a lot of books. Like every book I could get my hands on, especially sci-fi fantasy. I played Dungeons and Dragons as a kid, was very nerdy and read the "Monster Manual" backwards and forwards. But I think, if you had a difficult childhood, you can take two approaches to it. One is like, I'm going to get back on the world and be mean to people like they were mean to me, which is obviously not good. I took the other approach.

MD: What do you think was the pivotal moment or reason? Was it a certain source of love that you nevertheless felt? Do you have any explanation for that?

EM: Because I read a lot of books.

MD: So what writers were the most important for you?

EM: I got a bit depressed actually reading Nietzsche. And Schopenhauer. Really not recommended for a 13-year-old.

MD: Apart from that only very few will understand their books.

EM: They could be a little more upbeat. But then I read "The Hitchhiker's Guide to the Galaxy," which is really a book of philosophy that just seems like a silly comedy. And "The Hitchhiker's Guide to the Galaxy" sort of made the point that the universe has the answer. And that the difficult part, is asking questions.

What are the right questions to ask about the universe? And the conclusion I came to is that the more we can expand the scope and scale of consciousness, so that we're better able to ask questions about the answer, that is the universe. This is the right thing to do, I think. This is the thing to help understand what the hell is it all about. Why are we here? I mean, just step back for a second, what's the meaning of life? And that's not even the right question to ask. It's like, how did we get here? Where's it going? You know, all these things. So, we want to increase the scope and scale of consciousness so that we can try to figure out how to answer these questions, and what questions to ask.

MD: I remember when we were sitting together in Potsdam, at a very late stage of an evening, and I asked you about the meaning of life. And after a couple of seconds, you said: probably this wonderful French cheese.

EM: Exactly.

MD: Can you explain that?

EM: You need to feel life. The sensory experience of life, you can't get too caught up in the cold calculus of the cortex. You need to feel it in the limbic system, ask yourself, what does your heart say? And then take a moment to appreciate the many good things in life.

MD: You said a sentence that sounds very simple, but at the same time, incredibly beautiful. You said, "Without laughter, I cannot be happy." Can you describe that?

EM: Sure. What is laughter? This is a sign of a civilization going in the right way.

MD: The Catholics forbade laughter in the church.

EM: Did they seriously? Well, that's no fun at all.

MD: You can detect dictators and totalitarian, authoritarian people by their lack of a sense of humor.

EM: Napoleon had a good sense of humor.

MD: I'm not sure he was the nicest person in all respects.

EM: You know, nobody's perfect. Honestly, if you wanted to know someone, Napoleon would be a great guy.

MD: You once said that for you it's a terrible idea to imagine yourself lonely in a house. So, do you have a hard time being lonely?

EM: Very few people like being alone.

MD: I cannot be alone, but I know many people who would love to be alone. Or at least pretend they do.

EM: Humans are naturally a very social creature. And maybe what is defined as alone is not necessarily alone. I mean, if you're really alone and maybe just have books, not even communication, I think that's what drives most people crazy. I mean, there's a reason why in prison, solitary confinement is considered a big punishment. You want to have friends and family and someone — you ideally want to be surrounded by people you love and who love you.

MD: When we spoke last time about the big projects that you have, from Space X to Neuralink, to The Boring Company, to Tesla. I asked you, among all the projects, which is the most relevant for you. And you surprised me in a way, and then didn't surprise me with your answer. The biggest priority for me is AI, you said. Why?

EM: We need to be careful with the advent of AI. And who's using it, and who controls it, and is it going to be in the best interest of the people?

MD: The big question is, is AI serving the people? In the long run, will machines serve mankind? Or will mankind serve machines?

EM: Well, sometimes when I look at everyone on their phone all the time, I wonder, who is the master of who?

MD: You ask yourself that today? The German publisher Johannes Gross said 25 years ago: You have a cellphone? You can be reached at any time? So you belong to the serving people.

EM: Yes, people are constantly responding to things on their phone. They feel like they own the phone, but perhaps they should ask themselves whether the phone owns them. So, with every interaction we have, we're effectively training the sort of digital group mind. And I think it's perhaps less a question of whether AI is serving humanity or vice versa. Rather, there is a symbiosis. And hopefully, that symbiosis is one that mutually benefits digital and biological intelligence.

MD: When do you think the moment of singularity will be reached? This Ray Kurzweil idea, the moment when things will turn around?

EM: It's not far off.

MD: Then it is very much a question of AI governance. Is it in the hands of very few superpowerful players? And potentially one day in bad hands? Or is it in many hands? And is there lively competition? Is that the thing you're worried about?

EM: It's important to have some kind of government oversight. And generally, we agree that there should be a regulatory authority, whenever there's something that is a risk to the public. There are the regulatory agencies for cars, or aircraft, or food, drugs, that kind of thing. And we all think, nobody wants to abolish the FAA — we want them to oversee the aircraft. We want someone checking and confirming the aircraft is safe, and that kind of thing. Same for cars. For food and pharmaceuticals. So, it seems that we should also have regulatory agencies with some kind of public oversight ensuring that the public good is being pursued with artificial intelligence.

MD: Is it fair to say that a project like Neuralink was created in order to empower human brains? In their competition with artificial intelligence?

EM: Yes! I said jokingly that the slogan of the company was, "If you can't beat them, join them." So realistically, in the long term, we will not be able to beat the intelligence of computers. But perhaps we can achieve a happy symbiosis. And along the way, we can also cure a lot of diseases that are due to brain damage, either congenital or through an accident, or age, or whatever the case may be. So, if somebody has a stroke, or has epilepsy, or seizures, or clinical depression, or something like that, these are all things that can be improved with a brain device.

MD: You went pretty far with a vision that one day and, in the not-too-distant future, language won't be necessary. Because in theory, it is possible to read thoughts, to read desires of the brain, and in a way, translate them or implement them into actions — which sounds great and can solve a lot of diseases and terrible things and has already helped people big-time. On the other hand, that somebody would be able to read my thoughts. I don't know whether that is a vision that I really find desirable.

EM: No, there will still be privacy. It's not like they can just read your thoughts without your permission or anything. But what I do have to say is, the initial uses of Neuralink will for many years just be solving medical issues, serious brain or spinal issues. The first application we're looking at for Neuralink is to help people who are tetraplegics and quadriplegics and enable them to use their computer or phone easily just using their mind.

MD: And the vision that language could disappear or could at least lose its relevance. I mean we are seeing it with all the translation machines, which are helping to solve that issue. What is your vision here? How far can that go? And how fast can it go?

EM: Sometimes people get mixed up between what is possible in the long term and what is likely in the near term. The near-term applications for a brain machine interface are really just solving very fundamental brain injury, brain- or spinal-injury issues. That sounds like it's really pretty much an unequivocal good. Then, as the devices get more advanced, in the long term, you could do conceptual and consensual telepathy.

MD: Would you agree that there are three priorities, one being that we need to empower human intelligence, the second priority is, we need good governance of plurality, we have to make sure that it's not in the hands of too few. And the third priority is, we need agile regulation?

EM: Yes, absolutely.

MD: What role will China then play, with those other priorities? China has a totally different understanding. Everything that helps the well-being of the Central State of China and the Communist Party is supported. Ethical limitations, democracy or freedom and human rights don't play a role. Regulation is a kind of tool to help to make progress more useful for China's superiority. Isn't that a structural advantage for China in this kind of arms race with regard to domination of artificial intelligence? How can the West win it?

EM: First of all, my experience with the government of China is that they actually are very responsive to the people, in fact, possibly more responsive to the happiness of people than in the US. And when I meet with Chinese government officials, they're always very concerned about this. Are people going to be happy about a thing? Is this going to actually serve the benefit of the people? It seems ironic, but even though you have sort of a single-party system, they really actually seem to care a lot about the well-being of the people. In fact, they're maybe even more sensitive to public opinion than what I see in the US.

MD: That's the first time where I would actually contradict you. China doesn't care about human rights. How could there ever be an equal and level playing field. Do you really see an opportunity for Western democracies to win? What is your scenario, let's say, concerning the role of AI in the hands of politicians and economies like China, America, the West, the East in 10 years?

EM: Google and DeepMind, which is one company, are by far the leaders in AI, the ones making the most progress. So, I'm not aware of who would even be a close second, maybe open AI. So, China's putting a lot of effort into AI. And they may be making progress. But I've not seen progress that is close to Google and DeepMind.

MD: Let's see, I think China will catch up at light speed. Is the new administration in America going to fundamentally change its policy towards China? Do you think that Biden will provide more continuity with regard to China policy than people expect at the moment?

EM: I'm not sure what Biden's policies are regarding China. Some aspects of what President Trump did concerning his insisting on equity with regard to tariffs makes sense. I don't necessarily agree with all of the methods that he put forward, but with the concept of, we need to fight for low and symmetric tariffs. That's what we should really be doing worldwide.

MD: Do you fear that, in the context of this whole AI governance and competition, democracy could be weakened, or do you think it can contribute towards improving democracy?

EM: It has the potential to appear to improve democracy. We need to be a bit careful — democracy is not perfection.

MD: No, only totalitarian regimes can provide perfection. Democracy is always imperfect.

EM: Exactly. This is the nature of it, Churchill or somebody — Churchill has the greatest number of fake quotes attributed to him — said like, democracy is the worst of all the systems, except for the other ones.

MD: Another wonderful sentence comes from Thomas Mann, in his novel "The Magic Mountain": "Time is a gift of God's given to men, so that he may use it, use it, engineer, in the service of human progress." It seems that that is the shortest description of your life mission.

EM: I'm trying to use technology to maximize the probability that the future is good. And, at a foundational level, that means ensuring we have a future, which is why sustainable energy is so important for the future of Earth. And then becoming a spacefaring civilization and a multiplanet species is important for the future beyond Earth, to ensure, that in a worst-case situation, if there's a World War III or something like that, or global thermonuclear warfare, and maybe all civilization is destroyed on Earth, that at least it continues to exist somewhere else. And, the civilization on Mars that could end up being a stabilizing influence on Earth. But that, just fundamentally like the probability of consciousness as we know it, and life as we know it, lasting for a long time will be dramatically improved if we're a multiplanet species as a spacefaring civilization.

MD: We'll get back to other planets later, if you allow. The word engineer is very important to you. Almost more important than entrepreneur or founder or CEO or whatever. You define yourself as an engineer.

EM: I would say probably the main descriptive thing that I think is accurate.

MD: Which is in the end a creative product.

EM: Yeah, it's like developing new technology to solve problems. Science is great for science. Science is discovering things about the universe that already existed, and engineering is about creating things that never existed. I think to create something new that, as far as we know, never existed in the universe before. That's great.

MD: That's the biggest opportunity in life. And it's a new hierarchy, which, you could say, is very much in contrast to the old model of maximizing wealth, maximizing power. This is really about creating things and solving problems, which also seems to me to be the spirit of Silicon Valley.

EM: Yes, creating, problem-solving. You know, making life better and more interesting through technology, creating something that never existed in the universe.

MD: Nevertheless, there is an interesting development. Some people are leaving Silicon Valley saying it's getting too conventional, it's driven by too much political bias. That there's too much ruthlessness in abusing people's data. Peter Thiel left the Valley — you know him well. Alex Karp is very critical, and he provoked people with the letter that he wrote on the IPO of Palantir, criticizing the Valley. Where are you in this debate?

EM: You always have to be careful when things become like a professional sports team. If a team has been winning for too long, they get complacent, they get entitled. That's just how it goes. This is why you don't see the same team winning every championship all the time. It's hard and painful when people we know, when a team or group or location has been winning for too long, then it's inevitable that they start to get entitled. They start to take it for granted, and they can get complacent and a little bit full of themselves.

MD: This certainly has happened to Silicon Valley. Reed Hastings said in his recent book that a company should never see itself like a family or define itself like a family. It should define itself like a sports team. That's why you also have to exchange people if they are not contributing best, whereas in a family, you are basically helping even the weakest members in order to survive. If you share that principle, is the Silicon Valley community becoming too much of a family rather than a sports team?

EM: I don't think so. It doesn't feel like something is becoming like too much of a family. I've spent more than half my life in California. And where I'm spending most of my time now is actually in Texas. Because we've got the Giga Texas factory being built and the Starship program in South Texas. Except for Austin, I was just asking the team, where would you like to spend your time? Where are you willing to move to, because we have a critical mass of people who need to be willing to move to wherever we do a new Gigafactory. Or take our significant operation in the US. Austin was top of the list, so hence we ended up in Austin.

MD: What is for you the most important invention by mankind?

EM: Language. Sure, we've got to communicate.

MD: The first step is language. That was the fundamental distinction between humans and animals or lower forms of existence. And then the second step was probably writing.

EM: Writing was like having a hard drive, things could continue beyond the person. If you try to maintain everything with an oral history, it's very difficult.

MD: Exactly, only writing made it transferable. I would say the third step is publishing because that was a big democratization of knowledge. And you could say the fourth-biggest is digitization, because it accelerated it, made it accessible and global.

EM: Instant digital communication worldwide is really like humanity developing a nervous system. Whereas previously all communication was person-to-person, phone calls are still person-to-person, and mail was like a person carrying your letter to another person. And now with the internet we have instant access to all the world's knowledge.

MD: I'm super happy and surprised that you gave that answer — language — because it is always my answer. That's because I have an erotic relationship to language and writing and that's in a way fundamental to my job. I would have thought that you would answer that question with: the wheel.

EM: The wheel. Well, actually, the thing that really matters is two wheels with an axle — that's the big invention. In ancient times, we easily figured out that a round thing rolls easier than a triangle, but putting two round things together with an axle is not immediately intuitive.

MD: You being one of the most analytical and creative brains, is there anything that you absolutely don't understand?

EM: There are a lot of things that I don't have a great understanding of. I might have a good understanding of most technology. But I'm not sure I understand where humanity is collectively going. Are we going in a good direction? Or are we turning inward and just fighting amongst ourselves?

MD: What is the biggest challenge laying ahead of us?

EM: The biggest thing is that we are getting to a stage where perhaps our reach extends our grasp. We have all this super-advanced technology, but can we really handle it? This will be the test. This will be a filter for more human civilization: Can we handle the technology and not destroy ourselves? With all these advanced technologies, is it like giving a toddler a shotgun? We've got to make sure we handle this technology in a way that's good for the future. We're going to make sure we have kids so that they as humans continue to exist. We have to think what sort of actions we must take so that the future is good.

MD: When will we see the first human on Mars?

EM: Most likely six years from now, possibly four years.

MD: When will you go into space yourself?

EM: Probably in two or three years.

MD: Why do you want to be buried on Mars?

EM: If you're going to be buried somewhere, it would be cool to be born on Earth and die on Mars — just not on impact.

MD: Why is the SpaceX project so important for you? Is it the dream of a kid? Or is it a real kind of serious need for a plan B, because Earth could one day just not be the right place to be populated by human beings.

EM: It's not that Mars is a plan B — it's that we want to become a multiplanet species and a spacefaring civilization. Ultimately, with life throughout the solar system, and then beyond our solar system to other star systems. That I think is a future that is very exciting and inspiring, compared to one where we stay on Earth forever, until some eventual extinction event.

I mean, eventually the sun's just going to get bigger and evaporate the oceans. And so, at some point, we better do something. And I think urgency is important for making life multiplanetary, because this is the first time in the 4-1/2-billion-year history of Earth that it has been possible. And this window of opportunity could be open for a long time, and hopefully it is. But it might also be open for only a short time. And it's not necessarily that civilization will end, but our technology level could subside. It could be that we don't end with a bang, but with a whimper. And so, while it's still possible, I think we should take action. But Mars, to be clear, is not going to be some luxurious resort.

MD: It's a symbol for other areas where mankind can prosper.

EM: Mars is a real planet, so we can create a real civilization there. But in the beginning, it's a bit like Shackleton's ad for the Antarctic where he said, it's dangerous, you might die, it's going to be uncomfortable, it's going to be a long journey. Food probably won't be good. There's also this terrible terror, but it's going to be a great adventure, and be one of the most exciting things that ever happened, if you don't die. That would be my ad for Mars.

MD: What are the biggest issues that need to be resolved to make Mars a livable place?

EM: In the beginning, it's going to be very difficult because Mars does not have an oxygen atmosphere — it's got a carbon-dioxide atmosphere. You can, over time, convert carbon dioxide to oxygen. That's what happened with Earth. Earth instead of having oxygen, had CO2. The oxygen was mostly CO2, still a lot of nitrogen, and Mars has some nitrogen. So over time, we could go through this process that Earth went through with the CO2 and oxygen, with plants, and liquid oceans. I think it really needs to be warmed up. And in the beginning, we'll just be OK — we've got to create a little base, we've got to have the basics. We have to be able to grow food, and we'll need water. We've got to replenish the propellant for the rockets, because we need to send the rockets back so they can bring more people. Or those that perhaps don't want to stay on Mars have the option of returning to or visiting Earth. So, it's really about the need to get a lot of solar panels, propellant generation, food, all the basics.

MD: What was the most fulfilling moment in your professional life? And in your life in general?

EM: Certainly the birth of the kids was extremely profound. And from a company standpoint, getting to orbit for the first time was very difficult. Yeah, very emotional. We had three failures before that. You know, I'm the chief engineer of SpaceX. So, it's really primarily my fault that we did not get to orbit. Could have done a better job. But fortunately the fourth one worked. And that's all we had money for at the time actually. Yeah, there was much that didn't work. We would have been bankrupt for sure. So, I was so stressed out, and that actually didn't feel like joy. I just felt a sense of relief.

MD: Do you believe in God?

EM: When I was a kid, oddly, my father was like, Anglican, Church of England. I was sent to Anglican Sunday school, but then his partners in his engineering firm were Jewish, so I was sent to the Jewish preschool. It was also nearby, and it was a good school. So I'm singing "Hava Nagila" one day, Jesus the next day, and as a kid you're like, well I guess I will just sing along, you know. But I would say, from what I see, after reading all the religious documents. I do agree with some of the principles, like turn the other cheek. Basically, forgive people instead of an eye for an eye is a good principle. And love thy neighbor as thyself, I think is a good principle. But do I think all these stories are literally accurate? That seems unlikely.

MD: Why is music so important for you? You're a lover of techno music.

EM: I am, actually. I've liked techno music for a long time.

MD: That's why you go to Berlin?

EM: Simply one of the reasons. We have to have this great rave for the opening of Giga Berlin. Well, actually, we're going to start in the afternoon with sort of family music and everything, invite all the people that live in the region, have a vague sort of picnic, and then gradually get more hardcore as the night goes on. And then have a crazy rave till dawn, it's culturally necessary.

MD: Your recent track, "Don't Doubt Ur Vibe," seems to be your kind of personal anthem.

EM: To be frank, I made that with some friends as kind of a joke. And, you know, I definitely credit my friend Mike who was helping with that song. It was meant to be just for fun.

MD: For fun and encouragement of people. So, who are your favorite DJs?

EM: Well, I have quite a lot. Let's see. You know, like, Boris Brejcha, he's pretty good. I feel like naming a few is always limiting.

MD: Favorite clubs?

EM: Berghain is pretty good. I haven't been in a long time.

MD: It's closed. Should be reopened at the latest when the Gigafactory is launched.

EM: Sure. Sounds good. Swedish House Mafia is great. We will invite a lot of musicians for opening day and just have a fun party that has something for everyone, from families with little kids to young people. And so, there's no reason why the company has to be sort of corporate and boring. It can be fun. We want to make it fun.

MD: The bridge from Juan Atkins' beginnings in Detroit to the recreation of the Love Parade in Berlin. A frame for your opening?

EM: Yeah, we're going to have a good time.

Clubhouse Podcast

(2021)

Question: When are we going to get to Mars?

ELON MUSK: I think we'll get to when will we get the first people to Mars I think we have a decent shot of doing that in about I'd say, like five years, something like that.

Earth to Mars syncs up every 26 months. It's roughly the same quadrant of the solar system and when we can do an interplanetary transfer. We had one about six months ago, so in about a year and a half there will be another one. So figure, five and a half years.

We've got to make a starship fly to orbit and back repeatedly. I mean, the essential element is that you need a fully and rapidly reusable orbital rocket. This is the Holy Grail of rocketry. So no one has ever succeeded in creating a fully reusable rocket. It can't just be fully reusable, it needs to be rapidly reusable. So it doesn't take like several months of refurbishment between flights. It needs to be much like an aircraft where the main cost is fuel. You can't just be throwing rockets away every time. You need to have orbital refilling, where you can send the ship up to orbit then dock with a transport propellant so that you can load up to being almost full propellant and then go to Mars.

And if you've got a large, fully rapidly reusable rocket with orbital refilling that uses high efficiency, low-cost propellant then you can go to Mars. On Mars too you need local propellant production. So you take CO2 out of the atmosphere combine it with the water ice - H2O to create CH methane and oxygen.

And f you have those elements - life can become multi-planetary and we can have a self-sustaining city on Mars, which I think is one of the most important thing we could possibly do, for ensuring the long-term existence of consciousness.

I had an existential crisis when I was a kid trying to figure out what's the meaning of life? Why are we here? What's the point of it all? Is it all meaningless? I got quite depressed actually and sad about it. And then the thing that kind of broke me out of it was reading Douglas Adams's Hitchhiker's Guide to the galaxy. Where he essentially pointed out that the universe is the answer and really the hard part is figuring out what questions to ask about the answer that is the universe.

I'm trying to make fun of the fact that the answer is the easy part, but the questions are the hard part. So in order for us to gain a better understanding of what questions to ask or to understand what it's all about. We have to increase the scope and scale of consciousness so that we're better able to figure out which questions to ask and answer them. So the longer, the broader in scope, larger in scale that consciousness is, the one more likely we are able to ask these questions and figure out what that's going on.

Why are we here? To answer the fundamental questions, I think there's arguably a great filter that we face with as, will we become a multi-class species or not. We will be surprised if out there in our galaxy and others, there are a whole bunch of civilizations that prospered for a while, they might've prospered for millions of years, but then gradually the civilization collapsed for reasons external or internal. All civilizations go through an arc where they grow up in technology complexity, but then they don't keep going up. They, over time decline they fall and this has happened obviously. If you're a student of history of many civilizations in the past. You can look at ancient Egypt, years ago there was the great part of Giza, but then the people living there forgot how to build pyramids after a while, and then forgot how to read hieroglyphics.

There's obviously, Kevin's famous book about the decline and fall of the Roman Empire and how they had advanced technology in terms of roads, aqueducts plumbing and so forth and then they basically forgot about it. The ancient Sumerians, Babylonians, all have been all gone through a similar arc which suggests that most likely we will go through such ourselves and we'll be arguably less resilient to recovery because of globalization.

So I think, for the first time in the 4.5 billion year history of Earth, it’s possible to extend life beyond Earth and make life multi-planetary. This window of opportunity may be open for a long time. I hope it is, or it may be open for a short time. I think it would be wise for us to assume that it's open for a short time.

I'm an optimist, not a pessimist, but you have to say there's some chance it's only open for a short time and we should take advantage of this brief window of opening, where we can transfer, transport to make life multi-planetary and humanity is essentially the agent of life in this process. I think we almost have an obligation to ensure that the creatures of Earth continue even if there was a calamity on Earth, which as I said, could be man-made or it could be some natural calamity as if you look at the fossil record there have been many mass extinctions.

Question: Set up civilization there? All the way to like governments, rules, laws and everything?

ELON MUSK: Yeah, I think all those things need to happen just as they happen in the US and happen in every country. And I would not presume to prescribe what should happen there. I think the important part is just that we get people there and we get the equipment necessary to establish a self-sustaining civilization and at least one self-sustaining city.

I think that the key threshold of when we would pass the great filter is when Mars is sufficiently self-sustaining, such that if the ships stop coming from Earth, for any reason - it could be, something massive or something banal. And if the ships stopped coming from Mars, does Mars die out or not? It will survive for a while, but it will eventually die out. So it's kind of getting on us to pass that critical threshold where it is self-sustaining. Are we able to do that before some calamity or a gradual declining civilization occurs that prevents the specialist ships from going there? That's the key threshold, but in a more pithy way is like does the city on Mars become self-sustaining, which comes first? A self-sustaining city on Mars or World War III?

Question: What do you think is possible to build on Mars in 2 years after first arrival?

ELON MUSK: Let's start off being very tiny, just like a tiny little outpost. And by the way, it's going to be very dangerous. Sometimes people think, "Oh, is this like some escape hatch for people?" I'm like No, it will be dangerous, hard work. It's going to be you're out there on the frontier. There are far more ways to die there than there are on Earth. But it will be, I think fun and a great adventure. But it will not be a luxurious thing that is for sure, not for quite some time to go.

We've got to have a propellant plant, get solar power going, get the food production going start creating the necessities, iron, we need an iron ore refinery. We need, all of the sort of fundamentals of industry in order to make sure that Mars is a self-sustaining planet. I mean over time, like this would take a while, but you could terraform the planet and make it Earth-like, mostly by just warming it up.

Question: How do you think we should think about aliens?

ELON MUSK: Yeah... I'm trying to be strict in the scientific sense of the word, saying, "I've not seen a single piece of conclusive evidence." So that doesn't mean there aren't aliens.

I'm just literally saying I've seen nothing that could not be explained by other means. And where the probable explanation by other means is much more likely than this alien technology. And for people to say like their sightings of aliens. I'm like, listen man, the resolution of the picture needs to be at least like an ATM. Good. Okay.

Question: What is Neuralink? Why should we care? What is possible with it?

ELON MUSK: So the Neuralink stems from a concern I had where I was trying to figure out, even in a benign AI scenario, how do we at least go along for the ride? So for those following AI closely it's obviously improving dramatically. If you see like, say GPT- versus, GPT-2 versus, GPT-3, and just how radically that's improved, and there's deep mindset. I think they've run out of games to win at basically.

I still look at Tesla, it's an important thing to note. Tesla actually has, I think one of the strongest AI teams in the world, but it's AI team focused on real world usability.

So just really solving a vision perception and control with the AI. But even in a benign scenario for AI where let's say the AI just really wants to be super nice to us and make us happy. But we'll how do we stay relevant and have meaning, and at least go along for the ride.

That's in the good scenario. And then in terms of avoiding the bad scenario to the degree, we can couple a collective human will to the outcome of artificial intelligence and what's developed in that way. I think that'll probably be a better scenario than if we're unable to effectively couple collective human will to that outcome. So the final.. Okay, sorry, but this is getting kind of esoteric.

So people are already a cyborg and then in that. You already have a tertiary digital layer. You've got your sort of limbic system, which is your primitive drives and desires and responses. And then you've got your cortex, which is like long-term planning and thinking. Those are two biological lawyers. And then there's a tertiary layer, third layer. Which is digital and you already have that in the form of your phones and computers and all your applications.

You're far more powerful than a human would be without those cognitive enhancements, but the bandwidth between your cortex and your digital tertiary layer is very slow and, in fact, with the advent of phones it got even slower. So if you're thumbing like, say what's the bit rate of a thumb of a pair of thumb on a phone. It's very low, I mean, let's be super generous and say it's 100 bits per second.

Computers can communicate at trillions of bits per second. So at a certain point, computer get smart enough. Just like trying to talk to a tree. Trees do sort of talk but they talk so slow that we don't notice. We need to improve the bandwidth.

And with the direct neural interface, we can improve the bandwidth, between your cortex and your digital tertiary layer by many orders of magnitude. I'd say probably at least 1,000 or maybe 10,000 or more. And we could also spend a lot more time thinking about interesting things, as opposed to taking complex thought structures, compressing them down into words, which will also gain a very low bit rate and then having someone else receive those words, decompress them and then send words back at you. So a huge amount about brain power is spent in compression decompression and we could be instead spending it on deeper concepts.

And so, if you had a Neuralink, if two people had a Neuralink, you could do a conceptual telepathy where you have a complex series of concepts, and you can just transfer them directly uncompressed to the other person. This would massively improve the quality of communication and the speed of it. So yeah, then there are sort of pretty wild things that could be done, like you could probably safe state in the brain. And so if you were to die, you could, your state could be uh, returned in form of another human body or a robot body. Okay. This is getting like really, weird sci-fi stuff here.

I think you could decide that you want to be a robot or a person or whatever and you wouldn't be exactly the same. There'd be a little lost in transfer, but you could also say, it's arguably true that when you wake up in the morning, you're not exactly the same as yesterday.

Or the «you» of a month ago is not the same as the «you» of today. I mean a bunch of brain cells have died, some memories have faded some have strengthened, there are new memories. So anyway, the point is you wouldn't be. It could be something analogous to a video game, like a saved game situation, where you are able to resume and upload your last state.

Like in Altered Carbon. Maybe lose a few memories but mostly be you, so now that's the long-term stuff. In the short-term stuff for Neuralink, the idea would really just be to address brain injuries or spinal injuries and make up for whatever lost capacity somebody has with an implanted chip.

The first thing that we're going after is a wireless implanted chip that would enable someone who is a quadriplegic or tetraplegic to control a computer, or mouse, or their phone, or really any device just by thinking. And this obviously would be a massive enabler, make life way easier for them.

There have been primitive versions of this device, one done with like wire sticking out of your head, but it doesn't work all the time and you can't take it home with you. So just basically like in simplistic terms, I'd say it's like a Fitbit in your skull with tiny wires that go to your brain. So, Fitbit in your skull with tiny wires.

So somebody who's listening is good at designing, like Fitbits, Apple watches, phones, computers, various kinds. Then actually, they would be a great fit for Neuralink. We'll probably be releasing some new videos showing progress maybe in a month or so.

We have already a monkey with a wireless implant in his skull and the tiny wires who can play video games using his mind. He does not look like an unhappy monkey and you can't even see where the neural implant was put in, except that he's got like a slight, like dark Mohawk. But other than that, he's not uncomfortable and he doesn't look weird.

When the USDA person came through and inspected our facilities, our monkey facilities, she said it was like the nicest monkey facilities she's ever seen in her entire career, just FYI. We went the extra mile for the monkeys.

Well, it's a great team at Neuralink and they're making good progress. And like I said, I want to feel like the early applications will really just be for people who've had a serious brain injury like where it's like the value of the implant would be enormous. Because obviously the early implants will come with some non-trivial risk. And so it's gonna be like "Okay, does the good far outweigh the bad?" And then, that would be a candidate for some of the initial surgeries with full disclosure of like, little risks and everything, and one of the things really paying close attention to is the ability to remove the implant. So if somebody doesn't want it or it's not working, we can take it out and then re-implant another one. So we've tested implantation removal and reimplantation and it works great.

Marc: Switching topics, I mentioned kids earlier, as it turns out I have a very bright and inquisitive five-year-old who is crawling all over everything and trying to figure everything out and learning as much as he can, as fast as he can. What's the best way to think about educating a five-year-old in today's world?

Elon Musk: My observation is, my kids were mostly educated by YouTube and Reddit, and I guess, classmates and their lessons as well. But judging by the amount of time they spend online, it seemed like most of their education is actually coming from online.

I think generally with education, you want to make it as interesting and exciting as possible, what are all the things like say a good video game, does to keep someone engaged and interested. If kids can get super engaged in video games, its weird for them to be super engaged in education as well.

Like one of the things that, I think very fundamental is to explain the "Why?" of things. Like, so we're teaching this, but we're going to explain "Why we're teaching you this?" and "Why it is relevant?". We've evolved to forget things that are irrelevant or have low relevance probability.

It makes sense, otherwise we'd remember all sorts of nonsense things that weren't very important to our future. So if relevance is established clearly, then people will have a hard time remembering. If it appears to be irrelevant, it might be irrelevant, but if it's not explained to them, they won't know. And if you're trying to say problem-solving some sort of engaging narrative for the problem-solving... It's far better to say okay we're going to teach you how an engine works by taking apart an engine, and then putting it back together. And then let's find out what tools are needed in order to take this engine apart and put it back together. We need screwdrivers and wrenches and Allen keys, and we need a winch and a bunch of other things. And then you understand the relevance, this is much better than having say a course on wrenches or a course on screwdrivers.

You just start with a problem and say "What tools do I need to solve this problem?". That establishes relevance and gives a compelling narrative thread.

And then let's see, how can we make this engine better? What do we need to do? Okay let's calculate ... you know, if it gasoline engine, how do you get to a higher RPM or a better compression ratio? I'm using like outdated analogy of engines, but you could say "For electric motor, what steps would you need to take to get higher torque? Higher power out of this electric motor?" And then you can explain it's obvious why, things like Maxwell's equations become necessary in that situation.

Question: Would love to just get your take on where you see, the future for Tesla. And, especially, when it comes to battery technology and self-driving. Those two types of thing a lot of people are very interested in.

ELON MUSK: Okay, so you're asking me about the future of batteries and self-driving?

We actually have a Tesla model S sitting outside our house right now. It carries us and our two-year-old baby around and we love it. I mean, our goal with Tesla is, and has been from the beginning to accelerate the advent of sustainable energy. So in order to do that, we've got to make a lot of cars. We've got to make them increasingly affordable. Our rough target is - we want to be able to eventually make 20 million cars a year. And the reason for that is the 2 billion active cars and trucks on the road. I figure, you're not really moving the needle unless you're changing 1% of the existing fleet. So that's roughly how we came up with 20 million cars, and trucks per year. That's very important to accelerate delve into sustainable energy. And of course, we've got stationary battery packs and solar, making a lot of progress on that front. So yeah we're going to try to grow car production as fast as possible, and that the primary limiting factor there is battery cell production.

So, we're getting as much as possible from suppliers, but even that is not enough, so we're actually going to be building our battery cells ourselves. But it's important to emphasize that our suppliers who are great, we've got great suppliers and we're not trying to put them out of business. We want them to increase their rate as well, so, Panasonic LG and CATL. But to accelerate sustainable energy further, we're making our own cells and we're pretty excited about that. I think you expect possibly an acceleration of compound annual growth at least aspirationally. That's our goal.

And then combined that with autonomy, it's a very powerful story because once you have autonomy of self-driving cars, you massively increased the utility of any given car. A typical car is driven about, 12 hours a week. Depending on the situation, where you live, it's like maybe an hour and a half a day or something like that or in LA it might be two hours a day. So roughly 12 hours a week. And there's 168 hours in a week in a seven-day week, so most likely, cars that are autonomous could maybe do a third of the hours in the week or something like that. So, maybe they do, I don't know 60 hours a week of usage instead of 12.

So you got basically a 5x increase in asset utilization there and far less need for parking lots, parking garages and that kind of thing. This is in itself good for the environment, because you need fewer cars to get the same thing done. We would need fewer parking garages and places just to keep cars when they're not in use, because they're just being in use a lot more. The net of having a lot of cars times automation or time self-driving, I think is at the heart of why a lot of investors think Tesla is worth what it is. They're giving us a lot of credit for future execution, I think the trend is quite positive.

And I'd like to once again say if anyone is interested in practical AI where the rubber hit the road please join Tesla's autopilot's AI team. I think people not quite appreciate that Tesla has some of the most advanced AI in the world, both on the software side and on the hardware side. On the hardware side, we've obviously got our inference computer, which I think is still the best inference computer out there. Even though it's been going for a couple of years and we're building Dojo, which will be the most powerful training computer, because it's got to process vast amounts of video training data... Bringing the day of self-driving sooner translates directly to lives saved and injuries avoided because about a million people die every year in car accidents. And about ten million per year have serious injuries.

So that's the sooner, the better and a lot of lives will be saved and people's lives made better.

Question: Could you talk more about and why, you're not at a huge fan of LIDAR?

ELON MUSK: First of all, I'm not fundamentally against LIDAR on all things because for the SpaceX Dragon that talks with the space station we actually developed and built our own LIDAR for docking with the space station, so obviously if I hated LIDAR, we would not have done that and this is well before, this was like 10 years ago we started doing that. I don't have some sort of weird like, antagonism toward LIDAR. However for driving on real-world roads you have to solve vision. For basically understanding objects with passive optical photons, then making sense of those objects, so we need like vision perception what this objects mean, what they are going to do, what is the likely path of travel and then control the AI. The way we're doing it is by running a bunch of neural nets in our head. So we've got to run a bunch of neural nets to do the same thing in the car and at the point at which you've solved passive optical, and this is better passive optical than a human has, because you've got eight cameras, three of which point directly forward, two are diagonally forward and two that are diagonally rear and one rear. So the way we do it right now is we have all eight cameras synchronized, you've got eight frames collected simultaneously while moving towards and have in fact mostly moved towards. Video training, having eight surround cameras it's kind of a surreal thing to see, because really people have two eyes, but really more like one eye because two eyes kind of combine. Anyway, the neural net needs to move to full video training inference, surround video training, surround video inference, and then it will be superhuman, no question about it.

Because people don't have eyes on the back of their head, a human for all intents purposes has like one camera on a slow gimbal and that is often distracted, and maybe sort of drunk, or busy changing the radio or they fall asleep or there are all sorts of things that go wrong, there's no question that you can get be superhuman with just cameras.

I think if one is going to go with sort of active photon generation, I would recommend something in the occlusion penetrating wavelengths like radar, roughly four millimeter radar or something like that would be better if you're going to really delve into the arena of actual photon generation.

Question: People are very interested in how you work, you often, describe yourself as an engineer, so walk us through like its Monday morning, you wake up what does a typical work day in the life of Elon looks like?

ELON MUSK: I guess, I wake up and see if there are any emergencies by text or email and often there are. I mean, a ton of what I deal with is not actually fun or interesting, it's like a chore, so I've tried really hard not to do my chores, but then if I don't do my chores, things go to hell.

Yeah, that's pretty much how it goes these days. I do enjoy the in-person meetings more than email, in fact, I haven't, I think I'm getting slight like negative, like limbic reaction to email, it's killing me. Texts are way better to deal with and then in-person meetings are much better even Zoom meetings or whatever are better than email, anything's better than email frankly. So anyway I'll have a bunch of meetings. I'll write emails, write texts, especially if it's like an email to the group saying hey, we need to change direction, do the following things, and let me know if you think otherwise, but otherwise we've got to do these things and get our act together on this area or that area.

And then, a bunch of meetings. Most of my meetings are engineering and design, but, of course, we have to deal with finance and sales and other things that are necessary for a company to function. Quite a lot of context switching, so he sent me a meme of like "fear is not the mind killer, context switching is the mind killer," which I totally agree with, context switching is a real barrier, so I'm just trying to do less context switching, maybe focus on one thing for an hour and then another thing for another hour.

It's really hard to context switch between SpaceX and Tesla, and all the things that are going on in SpaceX to Tesla and then Neuralink, Boring Company which has fortunately pretty low bandwidth, they don't take a high level of CPU load because they're smaller and there's personal stuff and of course memes, you know...

Question: What does your calendar look like, do you allocate minutes back to back, do you have open space? How do you handle it?

ELON MUSK: I don't have a lot of open space, it's generally back-to-back meetings and it's insane, I mean my days are like insane torrents of information. I mean, sometimes I want to like audit what I do for a day and it's insane. I don't recommend it.

I mean, I was thinking like man, how long can I keep this up because I don't want my brain to explode and the meetings that are scheduled are not like nice to have, they're like these meetings that are essential. It's pretty intense. I was thinking maybe I should take a week off or something, like to clear my mind.

I know there is a bunch of people writing books on Tesla and SpaceX and it's pretty hard for them to get it right, because they just weren't there. Maybe I should write a book of my experiences, with all the foolish mistakes I've done. And like you know, some advice for others that might be helpful.

Question: Do you still sleep on the floor of your factory?

ELON MUSK: I only did that if there was like a crisis situation, and actually when the team is being asked to really work super hard, I gotta be right there with them and they got to see it, you know, seeing is believing and so if I'm just sleeping in the middle of the factory floor and I sort of go to sleep at four in the morning and wake up like four hours later, they literally see me, it's not hidden or anything and it's like okay. CEO's willing to take that level of playing, then they'll do it too.

Most of the time I did not sleep in the conference room because people could not see me in the conference room so I slept on the floor outside the conference room. Seeing is believing. So I mostly just sleep on the floor, outside the conference room so they could see that I was there.

I always wake up and smell like oil and iron filings, it was rough. Yeah, but I was asking people to really go all out, I can't expect them to go out if I'm not doing the same thing.

Question: You have your hands full with SpaceX, Tesla, the Boring Company and Neuralink, if you somehow magically found an extra five hours in a day and you had to start another company, what would you start?

ELON MUSK: Well I definitely have no plans to start another thing, my head will definitely explode. I think there are still tremendous opportunities in tunneling, for five years people ask me in what do I see opportunities and I'd say tunneling, and then nobody did anything, so then actually, initially as a joke, created the Boring Company, we did a test tunnel in LA and still people didn't believe us.

So, we just did our first operational tunnel in Vegas. The world really needs tunnels, all major cities have traffic and tunnels can massively improve people's quality of life, by making it easy to travel from one place to another in the city and then that can be further expanded to long-distance travel, where if you just draw a vacuum on the tunnel then you can go extremely fast, faster than a plane or a high-speed rail. So I'd really still recommend someone else please to start a tunneling company.

Then there's RNA or MRN'a, basically synthetic viruses which put at a good effect with Biontech and Moderna. But I think people don't quite appreciate that what's actually going on is the digitization of medicine.

So it's where you can just literally create an RNA or DNA sequence like a computer program and then, encapsulate that in a liquid shell, so it looks like a tasty treat for yourselves and you can literally do anything, this is absolutely the future of medicine.

You could probably figure out how to turn someone into a literal butterfly, your cells are biological computers, they execute just like old-school computer, where you feed it a tape or a punch card, your cells which are tiny biological computers, will do whatever the punch card says. That was probably a big eye-opener last year 2020, like just the understanding of the potential of RNA and then just super randomly, Tesla is actually making a fairly advanced RNA sort of micro fab or something, we're open to making it for other companies as well.

Question: Why is Tesla making RNA fab?

ELON MUSK: It's super random. About four years ago we acquired a company in Germany, they're very good at automation, they're called "Groman" and they're in Southern Germany. At that time of the acquisition they said "Look, we're willing to be acquired but there are just a couple of projects that we think of, even though they're not related to automotive, and we really like to continue, if you don't mind."

There are two projects; one is this like a tiny chip analyzer with tiny wires for analyzing chips that Intel needs for making CPUs and the other one is this Biotech thing that basically has three parts to it, there's a DNA multiplier, an RNA multiplier and something that puts the lipid shell on the RNA sequence. We are on version 3 of it now, they asked if they could keep it going, so if they keep it under 10 percent of resources - no problem, they can keep going. Then it turns out it may actually be useful.

National Governors Association

(2017)

Nevada Governor Brian Sandoval: Well good afternoon, and welcome Elon. Oh, I was going to take off my tie. Is that all right if I do that?

Elon Musk: I came with a tie, but then I was like, tall bit with a tie, so.

Brian Sandoval: Then we'll both be more comfortable.

Elon Musk: Sounds good. Well thanks for having me.

Brian Sandoval: I appreciate your being here today. You know when I'm with you, it's difficult to know where to start. Let's start, just what drives you? What is it that when you wake up in the morning, do you see a problem and you want to solve it?

Elon Musk: I think the thing that drives me is that I want to be able to think about the future, and feel good about that. So, that you know, we're doing what we can to have the future be as good as possible, to be inspired by what is likely to happen, and to look forward to the next day. So, that's what really drives me is trying to figure out, how to make sure that things are great, and going to be so. And that's the underlying principle behind Tesla, and SpaceX, is that I think it's pretty important that we accelerate the transition to sustainable generation and consumption of energy.

It's inevitable, but it matters if it happens sooner or later. And then SpaceX is about helping make life multi-planetary, and doing what we can to continue the dream of Apollo, and ultimately make a contribution to life becoming multi-planetary.

Brian Sandoval: Let's talk a little more about that. I think everyone is very interested that when you say, "making life multi-planetary".

Elon Musk: Yeah. That's exciting.

Brian Sandoval: It is exciting, so what's your vision there?

Elon Musk: You know, I think, particularly for Americans. Think about America is a nation of explorers. People came here from other parts of the world, chose to give up the known in favor of the unknown. So I think exploration, I think United States is a distillation of the human spirit of exploration. So that's why it appeals to Americans so much.

You can see this when there was a shuttle tragedy, and seven people died. That's terrible, but a lot of people die all the time, but why do we care so much? Because it was the dream of exploration that was dying, along with those people. That's why –

Brian Sandoval: You know, and I'm one of those, that probably like many of you remember exactly where you were when that tragedy happened. So you have 30 plus governors here today, and we're very excited about your willingness to be with us. You've hopefully heard me talk a little bit about my initiative, which is being ahead of the curve. What do you tell us as governors, what should we be thinking about in terms of innovation and developing public policy for the future?

Elon Musk: Well, it sure is important to get the rules right. In terms of legislative and executive actions, you know, it's sort of like, think of say, professional sports or something, if you don't have the rules right. If the game isn't set up properly, it's not going to be a good game. So it's real important to get the rules right.

It's worth noting that I think still in the United States the rules are still better than anywhere else. It's very easy to put something in place which is an inhibitor to innovation without realizing it. In terms of the regulatory environment, it's always important to bear in mind that regulations are immortal, and they never die unless somebody actually goes and kills them, and then they get a lot of momentum. A lot of times regulations can be put in place for all the right reasons, but then nobody goes back and gets rid of them afterwards, when they no longer make sense.

There used to be a rule in the early days, when people were concerned about automobiles, because that was a pretty scary thing, seeing carriages going around by itself. You know, you never know what those things might do. So there were rules in a lot of states where you had to carry a lantern in front of the automobile, and it'd have to be a hundred paces ahead of the automobile, there'd have to be someone with a lantern on a pole, like, okay. But they should really get rid of that regulation, and they did, you know. So it would really be awkward. Just regulations, even if done correctly and being right at the time, it's always important to go back and scrub those periodically, to make sure they're still sensible, and they're still serving the greater good.

I think in terms of tax structure, what is economically incented, and what is non-economically incented, just make sure that the incentive structure is correct. I think I'm saying, just totally common sense things here, but it's economics 101, whatever you incent will happen. So, if you incent one thing, that thing will tend to happen more than the other thing. You incent another thing, that thing will happen, and so the economics should favor innovation. This is particularly important to protect small to medium size companies, because it's sort like trying to grow a tree in a forest, it's real hard for a new company to grow.

When it's just a seedling or a sapling, it needs a lot more protection than if it's a giant redwood, or something like that. So, very important to give support to small to medium size companies in the innovation front. They're the ones that need it more than big companies. I think at this point, Tesla's almost a big company, the biggest company anyway, so I favor you know, supporting smaller companies than Tesla, relatively speaking.

Brian Sandoval: What would your response be, because there are critics out there with regard to incentives, and Tesla has been, and I can speak from experience, the beneficiary of incentives, economic incentives with regard to the Gigafactory. What would you tell those people?

Elon Musk: Well first of all, as you know those incentives were a little overstated. In the case of the Gigafactory, it's a five billion dollar investment, capital investment to get that factory going. I didn't know this until we did the press conference, actually that over 20 years, the Nevada incentives added up to 13 billion. I actually didn't know this.

Brian Sandoval: Now he's telling, go ahead.

Elon Musk: I learned it at the press conference, I'm like, "Really?" I mean, the thing is that they took what added up over 20 years and made it sound like Nevada was writing us a $13 billion check. You know, I'm still waiting for that check. Did it get lost in the mail, I don't know.

But you know, this is the way the press works, of course. Now if you divide $13 billion by 20, then it's like Tesla's on average, receives sort of a tax. Well, it's basically sales and use tax abatement is what it amounts to. So Tesla, we get on the order of $50 million to $60 million of sales and use tax abatement, divided over 20 years. But this is for something which has a $5 billion capital cost, just to get going, and then it would have to generate about $100 billion over that period of time to achieve a $13 billion tax benefit. Essentially, it's a little over 1% over that period of time, and that's great, okay, you know, it's not the way it was characterized in the press.

Because if it's put in the proper context, it sounds like, "Okay, well that's neat." It's about 5% helpful on setting up the factory, and about 1% helpful over the next 20 years, cool. That actually sounds pretty reasonable, and yeah, so that was helpful, but there are a lot of other factors as well. And we actually had slightly bigger incentive packages from some other states that were offered, but we factored in how quickly could we get the Gigafactory into operation? What were the risks associated with that progress? What would be the logistics costs over time of transferring battery packs and powertrains to a vehicle factory in California?

All of those factors weighed together is what led us to make that decision in favor of Nevada, and working with your team was great. It was very forward leaning. I think a big part was also just making sure if you feel really welcome, within a state. That's sort of what led us to make the decision for the Gigafactory, and then we have another factory in New York doing solar panels. Actually it will be the biggest solar panel producer in North America when it's done. Then we expect to establish probably at least two or three more Gigafactories in the US, in the next several years, as well as a couple overseas. The overall objective of Tesla is really, what set of actions can we take to accelerate the advent of sustainable production and consumption of energy.

I think the way I would assess the historic good of Tesla is in terms of how many years of acceleration was it? If we can accelerate sustainable energy by 10 years, I would consider that to be great success, even if it was only five years, that would still be pretty good. That's the overall chain of optimization.

Brian Sandoval: So you've talked about interplanetary travel, and sustainable energy, and the vehicles a little bit. What would you want things to look like in five to 10 years, associated with energy, and with autonomous vehicles, electric vehicles?

Elon Musk: Well I think things are going to be, they're going to grow exponentially. So there's a big difference between five and 10 years. You know, my guess is probably in 10 years, more than a half of new vehicle production is electric in the United States. China's probably going to be ahead of that, because China's been super pro EV. I don't think a lot of people know this, but China's environmental policies are way ahead of the US. Their mandate for renewable energy far exceeds the US.

I think sometimes people are under the impression that China is either dragging their feet, or somehow behind the US in terms of sustainable energy promotion, but they're by far the most aggressive on earth. It's crazy, everything. In fact the Coalition for Chinese Car Manufacturers has brought the Chines government to beg for them to slow down the mandate, because it's too much.

They need to make 8% electric vehicles, I think, next year, or in two years, or something. It's like they can't physically do it. So China's by far the most aggressive on electric vehicles and solar, but that's a common misconception that they're not. There's one Google search way to figure this out, by the way, it's really pretty straight, pretty easy. In 10 years, man, I think, so half of all production I think will be EV, I think almost all cars produced will be autonomous in 10 years, almost all.

It will be rare to find one that is not 10 years. That's going to be a huge transformation. Now the thing to bear in mind though is that new vehicle production is only about 5% the size of the vehicle fleet. So you think about how long does a car or truck last? They last 15 to 20 years before they're finally scrapped, so new vehicle production is only, roughly, at most 1/15 of the fleet size. So even when new vehicle production switches over to electric, or to autonomous, that still means the vast majority of the fleet on the road is not.

It'll take another you know, five to 10 years before the majority of the fleet becomes EV or autonomous. If you were to say go out 20 years, overwhelmingly things are electric, autonomous, overwhelmingly.

Brian Sandoval: Fully autonomous?

Elon Musk: Fully autonomous.

Brian Sandoval: So no one will have to touch the steering wheel if there is one.

Elon Musk: There will not be a steering wheel. In 20 years, it will be like having a horse. People have horses, which is cool.

Brian Sandoval: So having a regular car will be like having a horse, is that what you're saying?

Elon Musk: Yeah. Yeah, and there will be people that have non-autonomous cars, like people have horses. It just would be unusual to use that as a mode of transport.

Brian Sandoval: All right, let's talk about the energy piece, and rooftop solar, and storage.

Elon Musk: Well first of all, it's important to appreciate that the earth is almost entirely solar powered today, in the sense that the sun is the only thing that keeps us from being at roughly the temperature of cosmic background radiation, which is three degrees above absolute zero. If it wasn't for the sun, we'd be a frozen dark ice bulb. The amount of energy that reaches us from the sun is tremendous, it's 99% plus of all energy that earth has. Then there's the energy we need to use to run civilization, which to us is big, but compared to the amount of energy that reaches us from the sun is tiny.

Actually it doesn't take much, if you wanted to power the entire United States with solar panels, it would take a fairly small corner of Nevada, Texas, Utah, anywhere. You only need about a hundred miles by a hundred miles of solar panels to power the entire United States. Then the batteries you need to store that energy to make sure you have 24/7 power is one mile, by one mile, one square mile. That's it. I showed the image of this where, this is what a hundred miles by a hundred miles looks like.

It was you know, a little square on the US map, and then there's a little pixel inside there, and that's the size of the battery pack that you need to support that, real tiny.

Brian Sandoval: Well, you talked about 20 years from now, none of us, well some people, will still be using horses, or –

Elon Musk: It would be zero. It's so rare.

Brian Sandoval: So what would the energy piece look like? I mean, will there be transmission lines? Will there be a need?

Elon Musk: The use of energy is roughly divided into three areas. They're more or less equal at a high level. There's about a third of energy is used for transportation of various kinds, about a third is used for electricity, about a third is used for heating. Of the electricity production, call it something in the order of 10%, depending upon how you count it is renewable, maybe 15% today.

So that means that there's a massive amount solar that would need to produced and connected in order to be fully sustainable, because fully sustainable means you're tackling transport, non-renewable electricity generation, and heating. That means that we'll need to be a combination of utility-scale solar, and rooftop solar, combined with wind, geothermal, hydro, probably some nuclear for a while, in order to transition to a sustainable situation, which means, really for the most part, massive, massive growth in solar. It's going to be important to have rooftop solar in neighborhoods, because otherwise there'll need to be massive, new transmission lines built, and people do not like having transmission lines go through their neighborhood. They really don't like that.

Brian Sandoval: I agree.

Elon Musk: So you want to have some localized energy production, combined with utility, so you want rooftop solar, utility solar, and that's really going to be the solution from a physics standpoint, but I can't see any other way to really do it. Maybe I'll talk a lot about fusion and all that, but the sun is a giant fusion reactor in the sky, and it's really reliable, it comes up every day. And if it doesn't, we got bigger problems.

Brian Sandoval: Somebody asked me to ask you this. We talked about workforce today, but they asked me, are robots going to take our jobs, everybody's jobs in the future? How much do you see artificial intelligence coming into the workplace?

Elon Musk: Well first of all I think on the artificial intelligence front, you know, I have exposure to the very, most cutting edge AI, and I think people should be really concerned about it. I keep sounding the alarm bell, but until people see robots going down the street killing people, they don't know how to react, because it seems so ethereal. And, I think we should all be really concerned about AI. AI is a rare case where I think we need to be proactive in regulation, instead of reactive. Because I think by the time we are reactive in AI regulation, it's too late. And normally the way regulations are set up is that, a while bunch of bad things happen, there is a public outcry, and then after many years a regulatory agency is set up to regulate that industry.

There is a bunch of opposition from companies who don't like being told what to do by regulators, and it takes forever. That, in the past, has been, bad but not something which represented a fundamental risk to the existence of civilization. AI is a fundamental risk to the existence of human civilization in a way that car accidents, airplane crashes, faulty drugs, or bad food were not. They were harmful to a set of individuals within society, of course, but they were not harmful to society as a whole. AI is a fundamental existential risk for human civilization, and I don't think people fully appreciate that.

You know, it's not fun being regulated, it's not. It can be pretty irksome. But in the car business we get regulated by the Department of Transport, by EPA, and a bunch of others. And there's regulatory agencies in every country. In space, we get regulated by FAA.

But, if you asked every person, "Hey, do you want to get rid of the FAA and just take a chance on manufacturers not cutting corners in the aircraft, because profits were down that quarter?" It was like, "Hell no, that sounds terrible." So, you know, I think even people who are extremely libertarian, free market they'd be like, "Yeah, we should probably have somebody keeping an eye on the aircraft companies making sure they build a good aircraft, and good cars, and that kind of thing."

I think there's a role for regulators, that's very important, and I'm against over-regulation for sure. I think we've got to get on that with AI, pronto. And, there'll certainly be a lot of job disruption, because what's going to happen is Robots will be able do everything better than us. I mean, all of us, you know I'm not sure exactly what to do about this. This is really the scariest problem to me, I'll tell you. I really think we need government regulation here, just because you're ensuring the public good is served. Because you've got companies that are racing, that kind of have to race to build AI, or they're going to be made uncompetitive.

Essentially, if your competitor is racing to build AI, and you don't, they will crush you. So then you're like, we don't want to be crushed. I guess we need to build it too. That's where you need the regulators to come in and say, Hey guys, you all need to really, just pause and make sure this is safe. When it's cool, and working a bit, and the regulators are convinced that it's safe to proceed, then you can go. But otherwise, slow down. You kind of need the regulators to do that for all the teams in the game, otherwise the shareholders will be saying, "Hey, why aren't you developing AI faster, because your competitor is?" "Okay, we better do that."

Anyway, there's something like 12% of jobs are transport. Transport will be one of the first things to go fully autonomous. When I say everything, the robots will be able to do everything. Bar nothing.

Brian Sandoval: Let's move back to you're rolling out the Model 3 this year, right? How many quarters, what is that going to look like?

Elon Musk: It's going well on that front .We got, I think if somebody orders a Model 3 today, they'd only get probably late next year. We actually just started production, made the first production unit last week. The thing that is not well appreciated, something about cars, and any kind of new technology, is how hard it is to do the manufacturing. It is vastly harder to do the manufacturing, by factor of a hundred, like a hundred, than to make one of something.

With maybe 50 or 60 people, we could make a prototype of practically anything in six months. Now to manufacture that thing, we need 5,000 people to spend three years, and that's considered really fast. Manufacturing does this kind of S curve, where it's excruciatingly slow at first, and then it grows exponentially. But people tend to extrapolate on a straight line, so if it's real slow at first, they say, "Oh this is real slow, look at that. They're only going to make five cars a week, forever." Like, "Nope". It'll be 10 cars a week, then 20 cars a week, then you know, 40 cars a week, then 5,000 cars a week eventually. It just grows crazy fast, so we're hoping to get to something like 5,000 cars a week by the end of the year.

Brian Sandoval: Well I wanted to give an opportunity for some of the governors to ask questions, and perhaps some audience questions. I was told that you'd be willing to do that. So governors, any questions for Elon? Governor Scott.

Question-and-answer session

Governor Scott: Well thank you very much. We in Vermont have partnered with Tesla in terms of a power pack in our homes. For $15 a day, you can rent this for 15 years, and it'll carry power as a backup generation device for 12 hours. It's been really, really interesting from my perspective, but I'm curious about vehicles, and where we're going in the future, or how far in the future, do the cars themselves become the charging device? Like the roof, and deck lids, and hood, or do the batteries get so efficient, that you don't need that, and then you just power up for a week or something like that? Where are we going in the future with battery storage?

Elon Musk: I think the future, there's just those three legs to the stool. There's electric cars, there's a stationery battery pack, and solar power. With those three things, you can have a completely sustainable energy future. That's all that's needed.

On the solar front, like I said, it's going to be a combination of rooftop solar, and utility-scale solar. You'll need both, because of the enormous amount of electricity. Then, you know, one of the things that's been missing, I think up until now, is having rooftop solar that looks good. That's where we got the solar glass roof that we're developing, and we're doing it in different styles, so that it matches the aesthetics of a particular house, or a sort of regional style.

I think that's actually pretty important. The conventional flat panels solars for flat roofs, and for commercial will be the way to go. Putting solar panels on the car itself, not that helpful, because the actual surface area of the car is not very much, and cars are very often indoors. So it's the least efficient place to put solar, is on the car.

Governor Scott: Just wondering about maybe a wrap of some sort...does that make any sense in the future? Like a wrap of solar around either a building made up of solar panel, or a wrap of a vehicle, actually being the solar panel, or being the components of the vehicle itself?

Elon Musk: I don't think so.

Governor Scott: I'll scrap that idea.

Elon Musk: It's just way better to put it on the roof for sure. And I've really thought about this, I mean really, and I've pushed my team about, "Isn't there some way we can do it on a car?" I mean, technically if you had some sort of transformer-like thing, which will pop out of the trunk, like a hard top convertible, and just ratchet solar panels over the whole surface area of the car, extending for the entire say, square footage of a parking space, provided you're in the sun, that would be enough to generate about 20 to 30 miles a day of electricity, but that is for sure the expensive, difficult way to do it.

Governor Burgum: Elon, thanks for being here. With your background on payment systems, you understand the important role of the security in transactions. And now that you've got–

Elon Musk: I think security is a huge concern, cyber security?

Governor Burgum: Yes, and the vehicles you're building now are incredibly complex software systems. I mean the car is really a rolling piece of software.

Elon Musk: It is, it's like a laptop on wheels.

Governor Burgum: Yes, so share with us a little bit about your thoughts on cyber security, and how we protect us. You talk about protecting society when you've got a rolling fleet.

Elon Musk: I think one of the biggest risks for autonomous vehicles, is somebody achieving a fleet-wide hack. You know in principle, if somebody was able to hack, say all of the autonomous Tesla's, they could say, I mean just as a prank, they could say, "Send them all to Rhode Island," from across the United States. They'd be like, "Well okay ". That would be the end of Tesla, and there'd be a lot of angry people in Rhode Island. That's for sure.

We've got to make super sure that a fleet-wide hack is basically impossible, and that if people are in the car, that they have override authority on whatever the car is doing. So if the car is doing something wacky, you can press a button, that no amount of software can override, that will ensure that you gain control of the vehicle, and cut the link to the servers. So that's pretty fundamental.

Within the car, we actually have, even if somebody gains access to the car, there are multiple subsystems within the car, that also have specialized encryption, so the powertrain for example, has specialized encryption. So even if somebody would gain access to the car, they could only gain access to the powertrain, or to the braking system. But it is my top concern from a security standpoint that Tesla's making sure that a fleet-wide hack, or any vehicle-specific hack can't occur. They have the same problem with cell phones. It's kind of crazy today that we live quite comfortably in a world that George Orwell would have thought is super crazy. We all carry a phone with a microphone that can be turned on, really at any time, without our knowledge, with a GPS that knows our position, and a camera, and well kind of all our personal information.

We do this willingly, and it's kind of wild to think that, that's the case. The phone, like Apple, and Google, kind of have the same challenge of making sure there cannot be a fleet-wide hack, or system-wide hack of phones, or a specific hack. That's our top concern. It's going to become a bigger and bigger concern. I think Tesla's, I don't want to tempt fate here, but Tesla's pretty good at software, compared to the other car companies. So I do think it's going to be an even bigger challenge for the other car companies to ensure security.

Governor Daugaard: Thank you Governor. I must thank you for speaking to all the governors today. It's an honor to have you here. One question I had, we saw when gasoline prices went to three and a half dollars a gallon, there was a big jump in interest in hybrid vehicles, and you saw those vehicles become very much in demand. And then as gasoline prices have fallen, you've seen a reversal of that. I'm wondering to what extent you have a concern about the future of electric vehicles in the face of those very low prices? Can you speak to that?

Elon Musk: Well the economics, they kind of set the slope of the curve. So there's no question in my mind, whatsoever, that all transport with the ironic exception of rockets, will go fully electric. Everything, planes, trains, automobiles...Well a lot of trains are already electric, all ships, but it's questionable what that timeframe is. And the economic incentive structure drives that timeframe. That's really what it amounts to. You know, and the big challenge is that there's an unpriced externality in the cost of fossil fuels. The unpriced externality is the probability weighted harm of changing the chemical constituency of the atmosphere and oceans. Since it is not captured in the price of gasoline, it does not drive the right behavior.

You know, it would be like if tossing our garbage was just free, and there was no penalty. You could just do as much as you want, and trees would be full of garbage. We regulated a lot of other things, like sulfur emissions, and nitrous oxide emissions, and that kind of thing. It's done a lot of good on that front. With CO2, it's tough because there's so many invested interests on the sort of fossil fuel side.

Sometimes I think those guys feel kind of hard done by, because you know, it wasn't obvious when they were creating their oil and gas companies that it would be bad for the environment, and they worked really hard to create those companies. And then they feel like, well now they're being kind of attacked on moral grounds, when they didn't originally start those oil companies, or build them up on bad moral grounds. It is true that we cannot instantaneously change to a sustainable situation. Then those guys will also fight pretty hard to slow down the change, and that's really where I think is morally wrong.

Brian Sandoval: Governor Bevin, and then Governor Hutchinson and then we'll take some audience questions. Governor Bevin.

Governor Bevin: Elon, thank you for being here. The short version of the question, then slightly longer. The short version is, do you ever feel pressured by other's expectations of you, and your endeavors, in light of the progress you've made thus far, is the short version? And more specifically when you look just at Tesla alone, and you look at a company with a $54 billion valuation, and seemingly by typical market metrics, no justifiable reason for that. I'm just saying I'm curious – In all seriousness, do you feel a concern ever that your intellect, and your intellectual curiosity, and your ingenuity, cannot be be matched by those that are trying to commercialize it? Does that ever affect how you think, or decisions that you make?

Elon Musk: Well it is actually I find it quite tough when there are very high expectations. I try to actually tamp down those expectations to be impossible. In fact, I've gone on record several times as saying that the stock price is higher than we have any right to deserve. And that's for sure true based on where we are today, and have been in the past, so the stock price obviously reflects a lot of optimism about where Tesla will be in the future.

Now the thing that makes that you know, quite a difficult emotional hotshot for me, is that those expectations sometimes get out of control. I hate disappointing people, and so I'm trying real hard to meet those expectations, but that's a pretty tall order, and a lot of times, it's really not fun, I have to say. A whole lot less fun than it may seem, so yeah I mean, I don't ever sell any stock unless I have to for taxes, so publicly, I'm not going to take money off the table. I'm going down with the ship. I'll be the last to do it. I really wouldn't recommend anyone start a car company. I really wouldn't recommend it. It's not a recipe for happiness and freedom.

Governor Hutchinson: Mr Musk, Asa Hutchinson from Arkansas. Thank you for your frank observations about exploration. You know I look at the spirit of invention, and the spirit of exploration, which is really the hallmark of America. What is your comment on NASA, its mission? I was in congress, I supported NASA, but I always feel like it's floundering. It does not have the support of the American people that's needed. What's your comment on NASA, its mission, and what advice would you give us?

Elon Musk: Sure. Well first of all I should say, I'm a big fan of NASA. In fact. at one point my password was, ilovenasa. Literally, that was my password. You know, I think NASA does a lot of good things for which it doesn't get enough credit, and that the public, I guess, doesn't know that much about. Most members of the public, they're not really into hard science. It's not the thing they're tuning in for most of the time. I love hard science, but it's not that popular.

There's great things in terms of the telescopes, like the Hubble, and the James Webb, and you know the rovers on Mars, and the probes outer solar system. Those are all really great things. But to get the public excited, you've got to get people in the picture. It's just a hundred times different, if there are people in the picture. You know, if there's some criticism of NASA, it's important to remember, people in the picture.

You know, if you want to get the public support. But if you talk to a scientist about that, they're sort of like, "Well where is the science in that?" Like, you're not getting it. It's like, that's not why people are giving you money. I mean, it's a little bit of the reason, but the serious scientists are like, "People just make things more expensive." Why do we have people? Okay, well why do we have people at all? Or anywhere? Sometimes the scientists are the ones who just don't understand, even though they're smart people.

So you've got to have something that's going to fire people up, and get them real excited. I think if we had a serious goal of having a base on the moon, and sending people to Mars, and said, "Okay, we're going to be outcome oriented. How are we going to do this?" Okay, we gotta change the way contracting is done. You can't do these cost plus sole-source contracts, because then the incentive structure is all messed up. As soon as you don't have any competition, well okay, substantial urgency goes away, and as you make somebody a cost plus contract, you're incenting the contractor to maximize the cost of the program, because they get a percentage. So they never want that gravy train to end, and they become cost maximizers.

Then you have good people engaged in cost maximization, because you just gave them incentive to do that, and told them they'll get punished if they don't. Essentially that's what happens. So it's critically important that we change the contracting structure to be a competitive commercial bid. Make sure that there are always at least two entities that are competing to serve NASA, and that the contracts are milestone based, with concrete milestones. PowerPoint presentations do not count. Everything works in PowerPoint, okay I have a teleportation device, look there's my PowerPoint presentation.

So milestone based, competitive commercial contracts, with competitors, and then you've got to be prepared to fire one of those competitors if they're not cutting it, and re-compete the rest of the remainder of that contract. By the way, NASA's actually already done this, and they did it with the commercial cargo transportation to the space station. That was a case that NASA actually, an RF, they thought it would work or not work, but they didn't have the budget to do anything else. They're like, okay we're going to try this competitive, commercial, milestone based contracting, and it worked great. They awarded it to two companies, to SpaceX, and a company called Kessler.

SpaceX managed to meet the milestone, Kessler did not, so NASA re-competed the remainder of the contract to Orbital Sciences, and then Orbital Sciences got across the finish line. Now NASA's got two suppliers for taking cargo to the space station, and it's a great situation.

The same thing for commercial crew to the space station. NASA competed that in the commercial crew case, it's SpaceX and Boeing, and that's also a good situation. Now, I can tell you the SpaceX team is like, "We're going to do this before Boeing. That's for sure." Then like, I'll bet at the Boeing team, "We're going to do this before SpaceX." That's good, it's a good forcing function to get things done.

I can't tell you how important that contracting structure is, that is night and day. There's way too much in government where it's a sole-source cost plus contract. Again, economics 101, whatever you incent, that will happen, and people shouldn't be surprised. Okay, if that company manages to find some excuse to double the cost of the contract, they're going to get double the profit, because they're getting a percentage, so they're going to do exactly that, and also, they're not going to say no to requirements. So the government will come up with some set of requirements, 90% of them could make a lot of sense, and 10% of them are cockamamie that double the price of the project, but those 10% of cockamamie requirements in a cost plus contract, the contractor will always say yes.

Governor Hutchinson: There could be a future for you in government contracting at the state level.

Brian Sandoval: Let's go to Governor Hickenlooper, and then Governor Ducey.

Governor Hickenlooper: I think like most governors, I find it so refreshing to have the unbridled truth, but I do suspect every time you say publicly that the stock price is higher than we have any right to believe. I guess you probably get some calls from investors suggesting that maybe you don't say that so frequently.

Elon Musk: Yeah, that's true.

Governor Hickenlooper: I wanted to go back, and just briefly, because I think I wrote this down, that you said that artificial intelligence is the fundamental, existential risk facing civilization. Did I get that close enough?

Elon Musk: In my opinion, it is the biggest risk that we face as a civilization, is artificial intelligence.

Governor Hickenlooper: So, to a group of leaders, what would you advise? How should we be addressing something that's such a large landscape, and yet, obviously so important?

Elon Musk: I think that you know, one of the rules of government is, is to ensure the public good, and that dangers to the public are addressed. Hence, the regulatory thing. I think the first order of business would be to try to learn as much as possible, to understand the nature of the issues, to look closely at the progress that is being made, and the remarkable achievements of artificial intelligence. I mean last year GO, which is quite a difficult game to beat, that people thought that a computer would either never beat the best human player, or that it was 20 years away.

Last year AlphaGo, which was done by DeepMind, which is kind of a Google subsidiary, absolutely crushed the world's best player. Now it can play at the top 50 simultaneously, and crush them all. Just that pace of progress is remarkable, and you can see more and more coming up. Like the robotics, you can see robots that can learn to walk from nothing, you know within hours. Way faster than any biological being.

The thing that's most dangerous is, and it's the hardest to kind of get your arms around because it's not a physical thing, is kind of a deep intelligence in the network. You say, well what harm could a deep intelligence in the network do? Well, it could start a war by doing fake news, and spoofing email accounts, and fake press releases, and just by manipulating information. The pen is mightier than the sword.

I mean, as an example, I want to emphasize, I do not think this actually occurred, this is purely a hypothetical that I... digging my grave here. You know, there was that second Malaysian airliner that was shot down on the Ukraine-Russian border, and that really amplified tensions between Russia and the EU, in an massive way. Let's say if you had an AI that was hit with, AI is always to maximize the value of portfolio stocks, one of the ways to maximize value would be to go long on defense, short on consumer, start a war.

Then, how could it do that? Well, you know, hack into the Malaysian Airlines aircraft routing server, route it over a war zone, then send an anonymous tip that an enemy aircraft is flying overhead right now.

Brian Sandoval: Let's go to Governor Ducey, and then after Governor Ducey we'll finish our gubernatorial questions, and then two questions, quick questions, or one audience question and then we'll be done. We're running short on time. Governor Ducey.

Governor Ducey: Thanks Elon, I really enjoyed your comments today. As someone who spent a lot of time in his administration, trying to reduce and eliminate regulations, I was surprised by your suggestion to bring regulations before we know exactly what we're dealing with, with AI.

I've heard the example you used, if I were to come up with a colorless, odorless, tasteless gas that was explosive, people would say, well you have to ban that, and then we'd have no natural gas. You've given us some of these examples, of how AI could be an existential threat, but I still don't understand as policy makers, what type of regulations, beyond slow down, which typically policy makers don't get in front of entrepreneurs or innovators?

Elon Musk: Well I think the first order of business would be to gain insight. Right now the government does not even have insight. The right order of business would be a standard regulatory agency, initial goal, gain insight into the status of AI activity, make sure the situation is understood.

Once it is, then put regulations in place to ensure public safety. That's it. And, for sure, the companies doing AI, well most of them, not mine, will squawk and say, "Hey this is really going to stifle innovation, blah, blah. It's going to move to China." It won't. It won't because it's like, has Boeing moved to China? Nope, they're building aircraft here. The same on cars. The notion that if you establish regulatory regime, that companies will just simply move to countries with lower regulatory commerce, is false on the face of it, because none of them do, unless it's really overbearing, but that's not what I'm talking about here. I'm just talking about making sure that there is awareness at the government level. I think once there is awareness, people will be extremely afraid, as they should be.

Brian Sandoval: All right, one audience question. We'll take the first hand that came up. Oh, right here.

Audience: Thanks Elon. Ina Fried with Axius. Early on in this administration, you had argued pretty vociferously that it was best to engage, and better to be in the room, than not be in the room. Then when the President decided to pull out of Paris, you said that was kind of the last straw, and you were going to drop off. What drove you to that, and if you were still speaking to him today, what would you say to the President?

Elon Musk: Well I thought it was worth doing, you know trying hard to do, it was worth trying. I got a lot of flack from multiple fronts for even trying. Some guy rented billboards attacking me, and full page ads in the New York Times, and what not, just for being on the panel.

You know in every meeting I was just trying to make the arguments in favor of sustainability, and you know sometimes other issues, like we need to make sure that our immigration laws are not unkind or unreasonable. I, you know, did my best, and I think in a few cases, I did actually make some progress, which gave me some encouragement to continue.

But then I just really think that the Paris accord, man, if I stayed on the counsel, then I'd be essentially saying that, that wasn't important, but it was super important, because I think the country needs to keep its word. And, you know, it's not even a binding agreement, so we could always slow it down, the argument that there would be job losses, well we could see if there are job losses, before we exit the agreement. Maybe there won't be job losses, maybe there will be job gains.

But, there's just no way I could stay on after that, so, you know, I did my best.

Brian Sandoval: All right, well everybody if you would please join me in thanking Elon for being here today.

Elon Musk: Thank you, I thank you

Elon Musk Neuralink Demonstration

(2020)

Welcome to the Neuralink Product demo. I'm really excited to show you what we've got. I think it's going to blow your mind. The primary purpose of this demo is actually recruiting. So I'm going to emphasize this at the beginning and then again at the end. We are not trying to raise money or do anything else, the main purpose of this is to convince great people to come work at Neuralink and help us bring the product to fruition. Make it affordable and reliable, and such that anyone who wants one can have one. I want to emphasize the purpose of Neuralink, like what we are, what's our goal.

Our goal is to solve important spine and brain problems with a seamlessly implanted device. So you want to have a device that you can basically put in your head, feel and look totally normal and solve some important problem in your brain or spine.

And the reality is that almost everyone over time will develop brain and spine problems, these range from minor to very severe. If you live long enough, everyone's going to basically have some kind of neurological disorder. And these range from memory loss to brain damage, but the thing that's important to appreciate is that an implantable device can actually solve these problems. I think a lot of people don't quite realize that, but all of your senses, your sight, hearing, feeling, pain, these are all electrical signals sent by neurons to your brain. If you can correct these signals, you can solve everything from memory loss, hearing loss, blindness, paralysis, depression, insomnia, extreme pain, seizures, anxiety, addiction, strokes, brain damage. These can all be solved with an implantable Neuralink. This is an extremely fundamental thing and I think a lot of people don't quite understand that.

The neurons are like wiring and you kind of need an electronic thing to solve an electronic problem. Current medical research, we'll just go through what is the state of the art in medical research and then what's the state of the art in what consumers or people in general can get. So the current medical research has shown that you can read neurons in a human's brain. There's something called the Utah array, which has about a hundred channels per ray. But it's kind of a bed of rigid spikes that's literally inserted with an air hammer. You know that's slightly discomforting I think, and there are these wires and a box on your head. It's some infection risk and obviously it will look pretty weird if you're walking around with boxes on your head. And in order to use it, you have to have an expert medical professional there, and it's only been done on a few dozen people.

It served as an important proof of concept that this can be done. We did want to point this out and show that this actually does work. It's just not something that the average person could use effectively. And then in terms of what is currently available, there is something called deep brain stimulation where they put electrodes, a small number of electrodes in your brain and will actually zap your brain with an electric current. It's valuable for its uses, but it can't read or write high bandwidth information. I would say this is sort of like kicking the TV, which does work, but not always and it has limitations. Nonetheless, this is greatly helped over 150,000 people and despite being somewhat of a brute force approach, it has been very effective for a lot of people, and this is what's currently available.

We want to radically improve this by multiple orders of magnitude, improved by a factor of 100, then 1,000, then 10,000. Going into the Neuralink architecture, what we've done over the past year, is dramatically simplifying the device. About a year ago, we had a device which had multiple parts, including a piece that had to sort of sit behind your ear. It was complex and you wouldn't still look totally normal, you'd have a thing behind your ear. So, we've simplified this also, it is simply something that is about the size of a large coin and it goes in your skull replaces a piece of skull and the wires then connect within a few centimeters or about an inch away from the device. This is sort of what it looks like, this is that little device. That thing at the bottom is just to hold the threads in place, cause they're just like little fine wires.

I mean, frankly, to sort of simplify this, I mean it's more complicated than this, but in a lot of ways it's kind of like a Fitbit in your skull with tiny wires. Our current prototype version of 0.9 has about a thousand channels, that's about a hundred times better than the next best consumer device that's available. It's 23 millimeters by 8 millimeters. It actually fits quite nicely in your skull, your skull is about 10 millimeters thick. So it fits, it goes flush with your skull. It's invisible and all you can see afterwards is this tiny scar, and if it's under your hair, you can't see it at all. In fact, I could have a Neuralink right now and you wouldn't know, maybe I do. . .

It's also got all the things that you would expect to see, the sensors you'd expect to see in a smartwatch or a phone, like an inertial measurement temperature pressure. There's actually a lot of functions that this device could do related to monitoring your health and warning you about a possible heart attack or stroke or other damage, as well as a sort of convenience features like playing music. It can do a lot, sort of like if your phone went into your brain or something. Maybe that's not a great analogy. . .

All right, so it's also inductively charged, it's charged in the same way that you charge a smartwatch or a phone. You can use it all day, charge it at night and have full functionality. It would be completely seamless, and yes, no wires. In terms of getting a link, you need to have the device, a great device, and you also need to have a great robot that puts in the electrodes and does the surgery. You want the surgery to be as automated as possible and the only way you can achieve the level of precision that's needed is with an advanced robot. We are really looking for great people who can help develop both the device and the robot. We feel confident about getting the link procedure, the installation done in under an hour. You can basically go in in the morning and leave the hospital in the afternoon and it can be done without general anesthesia. In terms of getting a link like, it is essentially to open a piece of scalp, you remove about a coin-sized piece of skull and then the robot inserts the electrodes, we'll talk more about that later. Then the device replaces the portion of skull that was removed and we basically close that up with actually superglue, which is how a lot of wounds are closed. And then you can just walk around, right afterwards, it's pretty cool.

This is our surgical robot, and we actually ultimately want this robot to do essentially the entire surgery. Everything from an incision, removing the skull, sorting the electrodes, placing the device and then closing things up and having you're ready to leave. We want to have a fully automated system and this robot does actually the work, we have used it for all of the implantations.

This shows you a sort of close-up view, which I think is actually not too gruesome of the electrodes being inserted in the brain. If you look closely, you will see that it is a little counterintuitive, if the electrodes are inserted very carefully there is no bleeding. If you have very tiny electrodes and they are inserted very carefully, so that the robot actually images the brain and makes sure to avoid any veins or arteries, the electrodes can be inserted with no noticeable damage. You will have no noticeable neural damage in the inserting link.

Yes, you sort of think if you stab something with a wire, surely it will bleed, but actually at a really small scale, it does not.

So does it actually work? I'm excited to show you what I'll call the three little pigs demo. We are bringing out the pigs and what we're going to show you in pen number one is Joyce and she does not have an implant, obviously healthy and happy. Here is Dorothy and in her case she used to have an implant and then we removed it. This is a very important thing to demonstrate, its reversibility. So if you have a Neuralink and then you decide you don't want it, or you want to get an upgrade, the Neuralink is removed in such a way that you are still healthy and happy afterwards. What Dorothy illustrates is that you can put in the Neuralink, remove it and be healthy, happy, and indistinguishable from a normal pig.

Everyone just comes into this pen, all right, zoom in to Gertrude, the beeps that you are hearing are real-time signals from the Neuralink in Gertrude's head.

This Neuralink connects to neurons that are in her snout. Whenever she shuffles around and touches something with her snout, that sends out neural spikes, which are detected here. On the screen, you can see each of the spikes from the 1024 electrodes. And then if she shuffles around and touches her snout on the ground, or you kind of feed her some food, pigs love food, then you can see the neurons will fire much more than when you're not touching the snout. This is what is making the beeping sound. All right, cool, as you can see we have a healthy and happy pig, initially shy, but obviously high energy and kind of loving life. And she's had the implant for two months, so this is a healthy and happy pig with an implant that is two months old and working well. We said well, what if we do two Neuralink implants? We have been able to do a dual Neuralink implants in actually three pigs at this point, and we have a couple of them here. We were able to show that you can actually have multiple neuralinks implanted, and again, healthy and happy and indistinguishable from a normal pig.

It is possible to have multiple links in your head and have them all sending out signals that you're working well. All right, we just showed you a demonstration of reading brain activity and as I was saying, each of those dots represents a neural spike and the blue chart at the bottom is showing an accumulation of neural spikes in that region. So, in terms of additional brain reading activity, when we have say, one of our pigs on a treadmill and we take the readings from the neurons and try to predict the position of the joints. We have the predicted position of the joints, and then we measure the actual position of the joints. You can see that they're almost exactly aligned, so we're able with a wireless neural implant to actually predict the position of all of the limbs in the pig's body, with very high accuracy.

Now in terms of writing to the brain or stimulating neurons, we also need precise control of the electric field in space and time. We need a wide range of current for different brain regions, some regions require delicate simulation, some require a lot of current, and you want obviously no harm to the brain over time. Part of the way we analyze the stimulating neurons is with a two-photon microscopy. It is a very impressive technology, you can actually literally see in real time how the neurons are firing. The red things are electrodes firing, and then the green are the neuron bodies responding to the current from the electrode. You can see them lighting up different brain regions and then by carefully controlling electric field, you can actually have one electrode influence possibly 1,000 or 10,000 neurons. So although you might only have 1,000 electrodes implanted, you could be influencing millions of neurons.

This is just a similar chart showing stimulation at different power levels. So, like I said, for the initial device, it's read write and every channel with about 1,024 channels all day battery life, recharges overnight, has quite a long range. So you can have the range being to your phone. That's kind of important thing. This would connect to your phone and actually the application would be on your phone and would be communicating by essentially Bluetooth low energy, to the device in your head. That's why I say it in a lot of ways, it is like a Fitbit in your skull with tiny wires. As I said, you would not be able to see the device at all, you would look completely normal and just have a small scar under your hair. We are making good progress towards clinical studies, I'm excited to announce that we received a breakthrough device designation from the FDA in July, thanks to the hard work of the Neuralink team

I want to be clear, we're working closely with the FDA and we'll be extremely rigorous. In fact, we will significantly exceed the minimum FDA guidelines for safety. We will make this as safe as possible. You know just as with Tesla, while it is legally possible to ship a one-star car, at Tesla, the only cars we make are five stars in every category. So, we actually maximize safety and we'll take the same approach here at Neuralink. To emphasize again, what the goal of this presentation is, is recruiting. We want people who are great at solving problems to join the company and help us complete this device. Take care of the animals, write the software, create the chips and productionize everything. We need robotics engineers. We also especially need people who have worked on and shipped products. So if you've like shipped a smartwatch, a phone or any kind of complex electronics or device or advanced medical devices, we would love for you to contact us and consider working here.

A very important point to emphasize is that you do not need to have prior experience on brains. A lot of people think, well I couldn't possibly work at Neuralink because I don't know anything about how brains work and that's okay, you can learn. We need software engineering, mechanical engineering, electrical engineering. Chip design, robotics and all the things that a company needs to work.

Tesla on Q4 2020 - Results - Earnings

January 27, 2021

Company Participants

Martin Viecha - Senior Director, Investor Relations

Elon Musk - Chief Executive Officer

Zachary Kirkhorn - Chief Financial Officer

Jerome Guillen - President, Automotive

Andrew Baglino - Senior Vice President, Powertrain & Energy Engineering

Conference Call Participants

Colin Rusch - Oppenheimer

Dan Levy - Credit Suisse

Alex Potter - Piper Sandler

Joseph Spak - RBC Capital Markets

Emmanuel Rosner - Deutsche Bank

Ben Kallo - Baird

Gene Munster - Loup Ventures

Martin Viecha

Thank you, Sherry and good afternoon everyone. Welcome to Tesla's fourth quarter 2020 Q&A webcast. I'm joined today by Elon Musk, Zachary Kirkhorn and a number of other executives. Our Q4 results were announced at about 1 P.M. Pacific Time in the update deck we published at the same link as this webcast.

During this call, we will discuss our business outlook and make forward-looking statements. These comments are based on our predictions and expectations as of today. Actual events or results could differ materially due to a number of risks and uncertainties, including those mentioned in our most recent filings with the SEC.

During the question-and-answer portion of today's call, please limit yourself to one question and one follow-up. [Operator Instructions] But before we jump into the Q&A, Elon has some opening remarks. Elon?

Elon Musk

Thank you. So, just to recap the year, 2020 was a defining year for us on many levels. Despite a challenging environment, we reached an important milestone of producing and delivering 0.5 million cars. I'd just like to once again, thank the people at Tesla for an incredible effort. We delivered almost as many cars last year as we produced in our entire history. So, really an incredible growth rate and despite a very challenging 2020.

So, my hat is off to such a hard work with such great people at Tesla.

This year, we achieved free cash flow of nearly $2.8 billion after spending more than $3 billion on building new factories and other expenditures. We reached industry-leading GAAP operating margins in addition to positive net income and record cash flow.

Regarding capacity expansion, while we focus on execution, we continue to build a lot of new capacity. We started producing the Model Y out of Fremont and have almost reached full production speed. We ramped the Model 3 in Shanghai to more than 5,000 cars a week sustainably, and Shanghai continues to grow rapidly.

We introduced the heat pump to all of our vehicles. We ramped the single piece, we started and we're able to ramp to volume production at the single-piece castings for Model Y. This is where for the first time in history, the entire rear third skeleton of the car is being cast as a single piece in the largest and most advanced casting machine ever made.

We built a Model Y factory in China from start to finish in one year. We're also building Giga Berlin and Giga Texas, which we expect to start production later this year. And lastly, we built a battery cell factory in the Bay Area. And this even though it is a pilot plant, its capacity is large enough that it would be probably the top 10 battery cell factories on earth despite being a pilot plant.

Regarding the new Model S and X, we are launching and we're super excited to announce the new Model S and Model X are in production now and will be delivered in February. So we've been able to bring forward the Plaid, Model S and X. And Model S will be delivered in February and X a little later. The Model S Plaid, and we're actually in production now, and we'll be delivering next month.

So this is a tri-motor Model S with a completely new interior. There are actually a lot of great things about this. I'll do another call about the Model S later. But it's really a tremendous improvement over the prior version.

And the Model S Plaid will be the first production car ever that is able to go 0 to 60 miles an hour in under 2 seconds. So no production car ever has been able to get below 2 seconds 0 to 60.

This is a luxury [sedan] [ph] that is able to go 0 to 60 in less than 2 seconds, and will have the ability to seat up to seven people with the third row seats. So this is pretty nice. This is faster, to be clear, than any car. It's not like there was a different type of car, like a two-door sports car that was able to do that faster. This is the fastest accelerating car ever made that is allowed to go on roads in history. And like I say, we'll start delivering it in a matter of weeks.

And, obviously, we'll get into the details what the Model S changes maybe later this week or next. But it's really better in many ways. We will be actually raising the price of Model S for these new models, the new model will be $10,000 more. So, hopefully, people aren't too upset if they bought the old model last month, but this one is 10k more. Yes, we think it's probably the best car of any kind at any price available in the world today.

Then with regard to Full Self-Driving, we've made massive progress on Full Self-Driving. I recommend watching the videos of our public beta. So we've got, I think, almost 1,000 people in the beta at this point.

And with each successful release of the beta – of the FSD software, it's really improving rapidly. It's very common for me to have no interventions on drives that I do, including drives to a place that I've never been to. So these are not preplanned routes.

The car has never been there before. And it's now actually more common than not for the car to have no interventions, even on a complex drive. This is basically why I'm highly confident the car will drive itself for the reliability of a human this year. This is a very big deal.

And thinking about, like, how does one justify the value of the company being where it is? And I think there is a way, just with back of the envelop math, to potentially justify it, where if

Tesla's ships, let's say, hypothetically, $50 billion or $60 billion worth of vehicles, and those vehicles become Full Self-Driving and can be used used as robotaxis, the utility increases from an average of 12 hours a week to potentially an average of 60 hours a week, if they're capable of serving as robotaxi. So that's like roughly a 5x increase in utility. But even if you say like, okay, let's just assume that the car becomes twice as useful not 5x as useful, but merely twice as useful, that would be a doubling again of the revenue of the company, which is almost entirely gross margin.

So it would mean, it would be like if you made $50 billion worth of cars, it will be like having $50 billion of incremental profit basically from that because it's just software. It's like $1 trillion and the company is still in high-growth mode. So I think there is a way to sort of like justify the valuation of the company where it is using just the cars and nothing else, the cars with FSD. And I suspect at least some number of investors are taking that approach.

So in conclusion, while 2020 was a turning point for Tesla and in terms of profitability, we believe this is just the beginning. We think 2021 is going to be even more exciting. And you don't know what to expect in a given year. Obviously, last year, we did not 0 many things we do not expect. But assuming that '21 is a relatively normal year from an external standpoint I think it's going to be a great year for Tesla.

We've got a ton of many great new products coming out. We've got factories that are advanced factories set up for production. It will also make it easier having a factory in Berlin, one, in Texas second, just from a logistics standpoint. And Texas can help supply the eastern half of the U.S. and Berlin can help supply Europe. And there's just pure cars on both much less capital tied up with big cars that are been transported to customers.

And I think the fundamental efficiency of the company will be much better with the factories or at least having factories on on each continent and having 2 factories in the U.S. So I'm super excited about the future. And yes, we look forward to making it happen. Thank you.

Martin Viecha

Thank you very much. And I think our CFO, Zach Kirkhorn, has some opening remarks as well.

Zachary Kirkhorn

Yes. Thanks, Martin. As Elon mentioned, 2020 has been an extremely successful year while managing through many unforeseen and unexpected challenges. On cash, we continue to generate strong free cash flows, reaching a record $1.9 billion in Q4, alongside growth and investment for future programs. Additionally, we've been able to reduce our use of debt and various working capital lines, including settling $2 billion of convertible debt in Q4, which will continue into Q1.

For net income, we achieved our first calendar year and 6 sequential quarters of profitability. In addition, auto gross margin excluding credits improved from 2019 to 2020, despite reductions in ASP and inefficiencies from new product launches and transitions.

On Q4 specifically, this was a noisy quarter so let's unpack a few things. Stock-based comp increased, part of which is driven by the rise of the stock price over the course of our 2020 employee performance grant process and a portion of which is unique to Q4 only. The impact of SBC increases is seen across both COGS, as well as operating expenses.

Automotive gross margin in Q4 was primarily impacted by two things; first, we invested in improving our products built in Fremont, including converting over to the new Model S and Model X, launching the single-piece castings on Model Y and introducing heat pump on Model 3. Second, logistics and labor costs were impacted due to supply chain instability and pandemic inefficiencies.

Adjusting for items such as these as we do in our internal management views, we saw an improvement in auto gross margin. Our services and other P&L was impacted by many of the same factors just mentioned, including onboarding costs associated with new service capacity. However, what's most important here is that we've accelerated the growth in service capacity and we’ll continue to drive capacity expansion as fast as possible.

On energy gross margin, we saw an impact from Solar Roof related ramp costs and typical seasonality in the lease PPA business. OpEx as a percentage of revenue continues to reduce despite impacts from items mentioned, as well as increased investment in development of future products.

Finally, the early settlement of our convertible notes resulted in an additional $100 million of interest expense for the quarter. All that being said, nothing has changed about our view that operating margin will continue to grow and remain industry leading.

As we look forward, 2021 may be our most meaningful step forward yet, as we see the benefits of long-standing investments in capacity and technology. The range of possible outcomes this year is wide, given the magnitude of launches. That's a few things we should keep in mind.

We continue to expect a long-term volume CAGR of 50%, of which we may materially exceed this in 2021. As we increase production rates, volumes will skew towards the second half of the year, and ramp inefficiencies will be a part of this year's story and are necessary to achieve our long-term goals.

Specifically for Q1, our volumes will have the benefit of early Model Y ramp in Shanghai, However, S and X production will be low due to the transition to the newly architected products. Additionally, we're working extremely hard to manage through the global semiconductor shortage, as well as port capacity, which may have a temporary impact.

We will continue to invest heavily in supercharging and service capacity while driving reductions on cost, including OpEx as a percentage of revenue. Global demand continues to outpace production, and we're moving as quickly as we can with a focus on the long-term. I look forward to providing updates on progress throughout the year.

Question-and-Answer Session

A - Martin Viecha

Thank you very much. And now we can jump straight into questions. The first question from institutional investors is, what is currently holding Tesla back from being the market share leader in solar?

Elon Musk

Yeah. So we're actually seeing tremendous growth in solar quarter-over-quarter last year. And we had our best quarter since, I think, 2018 in Q4. So we do actually expect to become the market leader in solar and then go far beyond it. Unfortunately, there were a few years there where we had to devote the whole company to Model 3 production and building.

We basically took the whole company, including people that work around solar and have work on cars. But now we got a little more bandwidth, we're putting a lot of attention on solar, and it is growing rapidly. So I think it will not be long before Tesla is, by far, the market leader in solar.

Zachary Kirkhorn

Another really important part of the solar strategy is achieving an industry-leading cost structure, which then allows us to have industry-leading pricing. And so that's something that we've accomplished over the last year in terms of getting the cost structure in the place that it needs to be and I think I've mentioned, this is a really important part industry-leading pricing to become the leader in the space.

Elon Musk

Yes. And actually important part is achieving better integration between the Tesla Powerwall and the Tesla Retrofit Solar and Tesla Roof. And we're confident we'll have excellent integration – excellent integration with the Powerwall and Tesla Solar, whether it's retrofit or but [indiscernible] roof before the end of the year.

So it's really – I think we've got a good strategy. As Zach mentioned, we're focused on reducing the amount of time and the complexity of the install, and we're making great progress in that regard. And I think we'll have something that's really dialed in this year.

Martin Viecha

Thank you. The second question is, could current owners get ability to transfer their FSD to their next vehicle? This would be a huge for loyalty and overall increased sales of vehicles who are offering more FSD sales on used vehicles.

Elon Musk

Unfortunately, we're not considering that at this time. We do actually offer an increased – higher price than for a car with FSD than one without FSD. And I do think that the market currently undervalues – or the consumer market. And arguably the stock market sales probably undervalue the just how good FSD is going to be. But we're not currently planning on offering – on allowing it to get transferred.

Martin Viecha

Thank you.

Elon Musk

We will be offering subscription pretty soon in the next month or two. So that should address a lot of people's concerns for being able to get it.

Martin Viecha

Thank you very much. And the third question is, can you give us a progress update on dry coating of the battery electrode?

At the Battery Day, Elon said, 'I would not say this is completely in the bag as – yet as the yields were low.'

Elon Musk

Andrew?

Andrew Baglino

Yes. Sure. It's true. The in-house cell manufacturing system we revealed at Battery Day contains new processes and equipment. So we did expect some unknown unknowns and technical challenges to arise through the production ramp. The Kato team, however, has been able to solve each manufacturing problem presented to date, and continues to improve yield and rate week-over-week and month-over-month as we move up the production S-Curve.

At the same time, the cell engineering teams refined designs, and deepened understanding has reinforced our confidence in the drive process and 4680 design, meeting our performance and cost targets. And from a capacity perspective, we have 10 gigawatt hours worth of equipment landed at Kato. The production staff is nearly all hired. Our material supply chain is established and the team is on track for full production ramp this year. Meanwhile, we've developed enough engineering confidence with our 4680 design and the production process and equipment to kick off manufacturing equipment and facility construction to support our 100 gigawatt hour 2022 goal.

Martin Viecha

Okay. Thank you very much. The next question is, why are you confident Tesla will achieve Level 5 autonomy in 2021? And why is Dojo not necessary to get there?

Elon Musk

I guess, I'm confident based on my understanding of the technical roadmap and the progress that we're making between each beta iteration. Yes. As I'm saying, it's not remarkable at all for the car to completely drive you from one location to another through a series of complex intersections. It's now about just improving the corner case reliability and getting it to 99.9999% reliable with respect to an accident.

Basically, we need to get it to better than human by a factor of at least 100% or 200%. And this is happening rapidly because we've got so much training data with all the cars in the field. And the software is improving dramatically. We also write the software for labeling. And I'll say it's quite challenging. We're moving everything towards video labeling. So, all video labeling for video inference and so there are still a few [indiscernible] that need to be upgraded to video training and video inference.

And really, as we transition to each net to video, the performances become exceptional. So, this is like a hot thing. The video, the labeling software that we work for, video labeling, making that better has a huge effect on the efficiency of labeling. And then, of course, the Holy Grail is auto labeling. So, we put a lot of work into having the labeling tool to be more efficient when used by a person, as well as enabling auto labeling where we can.

Dojo is a training supercomputer. We believe it will be, we think it may be the best neural net training computer in the world by possibly an order of magnitude. So, it is a whole thing in and of itself. And this is something which we offer potentially as a service. So, some of the others need neural net training, we're not trying to keep it to ourselves.

So, I think there could be a whole line of business in and of itself. And then, of course, for training vast amounts video data and getting the reliability from 100% to 200% better than average human to 2,000% better than average human. So, that will be very helpful in that regard.

Martin Viecha

Thank you. The next question is what is Tesla's current gigawatt-hour run rate of the 4680 cell production? How do you see this run rate evolving by mid-2021 or end of 2021?

Elon Musk

I think we kind of talked about that true. I mean essentially, what we're saying is that the number to think about or focus on is like we've got a 100 gigawatt-hour total Tesla cells produced in 2022. It's not that important to look at the run up to that because these things tend to improve exponentially. But we are installing capacity in 2022 for 200 gigawatt hours a year and we think probably we should be able to achieve 30% of targeted design capacity in 2022.

Zachary Kirkhorn

Yes. Agreed, Elon. And as you've said before, with the S curve of production, you can be off a little bit on the initial part of the S curve, and that makes a difference in absolute capacity by quite a bit, one month to the next. So, yes, I mean we are progressing up that S curve as fast as we possibly can.

Elon Musk

Yes. And we don't see any showstoppers.

Zachary Kirkhorn

Yes.

Martin Viecha

Thank you very much. And one more question is from retail investors. What is Tesla doing to improve service experience? Tesla had a reputation for outstanding customer service. Now it's impossible to even call a service center, and appointments are scheduled weeks out.

Jerome Guillen

Yes. Well, as far as best service, no service. So we spent a lot of efforts trying to improve the quality and the reliability of our cars. In the last two years, the frequency of service visits are reduced by one-third. So customers have to come less frequently in service, which is really the goal, no service. And if service has to take place, we are trying to make it as painless as possible.

One big effort there is to increase mobile service, which is now more than 40% of all visits in North America. We're trying to push that to 50% this year. In 50% of service visits lasts less than two hours. So we're trying to service the cars very quickly, so people can get their vehicles back on the road.

And in terms of service appointment, it continues to improve. We have actually 140 service centers right now in North America. For 100 out of those 140, you can get appointments in less than 10 days. And we're going to make sure that all service centers have a short wait time.

We're accelerating, as Zach mentioned earlier, the pace of opening. In North America, we opened 11 centers in December, and we have plans to open 46 in the first half of this year. So that's what we're doing to improve service.

In terms of phones, our emphasis is on the app. Really, we want all communications to go through the app, the tesla app.

And we are trying to move away from the phone. As the app is much better than the phone.

It can spot directly alerts, directly from the car and schedule a service appointment. And there is a written record of all communication between the customer and the service team. You can have pictures in there. You can take care of your payment without entering the credit card and doing all that stuff. You get updates on the service.

And there is even more features that are going to come in the coming months on the app. And I think everybody will be happy, including the ability to spot where your service technician is and how far it is to coming from your car and what's going on there. So we are investing everything on the app. I think just like most other companies as well, and that's the way of the

Martin Viecha

Thank you very much. And now let's go to institutional investor questions. The question number one, what are the key milestones we need to achieve in order to evolve current FSD to a commercial Level 4, Level 5 ridesharing solution?

Elon Musk

Yes, so it really goes back to what I was saying a moment ago, which is, we need to transition over the neural nets in the car to video. And in order to do that, the whole stack has to be changed to video. That means gathering video clips than using it and this is actually surround video.

You've got 8 cameras operating simultaneously with synchronized frame rates. You've got 8 frame surround video. And then you've got to label basically everything in that video snippet and then train against that and have those neural nets operate the car.

This is coming from the past where we would label, the neural nets would be a single camera, single frame. So no video and not combining the cameras. And then we went from single frame, one frame at a time, one camera at a time, neural nets to surround camera, neural nets would look at all 8 cameras but only 1 frame at a time, and now to where we include the time dimension, and that's video.

So I really do see this as a question of getting work done. We're getting it done. And you can see the results in the rapidly improving FSD betas, we're also going to be expanding the FSD beta itself to include more and more people. So from my standpoint, it looks like a very clear and obvious path towards a vehicle that will drive 100% safer than a person. Yes. I really don't see any obstacles here.

Martin Viecha

Thank you. And the second question from institutionals is, does Tesla plan or expect to license any of its software applications, FSD and auto bidder in particular, to third-party OEMs?

Elon Musk

I think we're very open to licensing our software to third parties. And we've had some preliminary discussions about licensing autopilot to other OEMs. So this is something we're more than happy to do. And I think, obviously, like we need to probably do a little bit more work to prove that Tesla Autopilot is capable of full self-driving, which is, I think, will become obvious later this year. And then we're more than happy to license that to other car companies.

We're definitely not trying to keep it to be a Tesla exclusive situation. And I think the probably same goes for Autobidder. We haven't thought as much about Autobidder, but the Tesla philosophy is definitely not to create walled gardens. We're going to allow other companies to use our supercharge networks. And yes, using our autonomy software and Autobidder be fine to.

Martin Viecha

Thank you. The next question is, key differences in product, customer preferences, FSD strategy between China and the rest of the world. Do we need to do things differently to win the Chinese EV market?

Elon Musk

Well, we currently are winning that, we are currently the leader in the Chinese EV market. So I think we're mostly doing something right if we're the best-selling electric car in China.

That said, very few of our customers in China, I think maybe as low as 1% or 2%, actually have selected the FSD option. This is much lower than rest of world. So we definitely need to make it work well in China. I think some of it works well in China, then we will have a Grade 4 FSD.

I find that the customers in China, Tesla owners in China are among the most discerning in the world. Their attention to detail is incredible. So, I'm confident that they will buy FSD as soon as it’s working on time. And we hopefully that is later this year.

Martin Viecha

Thank you. And the next question is, is it fair to argue that the best way to think about company's long-term earnings power is tied to profit per unit of battery capacity? Three-terawatt hours target from Battery Day implies half of long-term battery capacity goes to storage, depending on what you assume for pack size on Elon's 20 million vehicle unit goal?

Elon Musk

Yeah. It is. So the fundamental limit on electric vehicles right now, in general, is total availability of cells. What's the output of factory cells in gigawatt hours? And you can't grow faster than that. Now at Tesla, we've improved the efficiency of cars dramatically, such that you can actually get a pretty good range even with the standard range battery pack.

It's approaching for Model 3, it's approaching the high 200s. And some slight continued improvements, we'll start to get to a 300-mile range even with standard pack and an order 500 kilometers.

So there's efficiency improvements in the car. But fundamentally, the growth is dependent on cell production. And there's, obviously, a lot of other companies that have a need for sales.

But the reason Tesla is doing its own cell production is in order to accelerate the growth. It is not to make less use of our cell suppliers. In fact, I want to be really clear, Tesla wants to increase purchases from cell suppliers. And we've been very clear with our cell suppliers, whether it be CATL or Panasonic or LG that we will take as many batteries as they can produce.

We urge them to increase their production, and we will buy as much as they can send to us. Obviously, there are some price limits on that because the car still needs to be affordable. But I'm just trying to be as clear as possible that our goal with making our own cells is not to disintermediate our suppliers. It is to supplement our suppliers. And we went to our suppliers of cells to increase their production, and in addition have our production that is simply taking up the amount beyond, which they are either unable or unwilling to increase their production.

So it's an acceleration over and above the most that our suppliers say they can produce for us. Since the cell output drives vehicle output, I mean probably the Roadster value of Tesla is just what's the cell output that implies vehicle output, and then at least double that for autonomy revenue probably one level. And that's how you figure out the value of the company, I think, long term.

Martin Viecha

Thank you very much. The next question is about 4680 cells which we already covered in the retail section of this call. So let's go straight to the last question from institutional investors, which is, where are you in Cybertruck development? What are your expectations for Cybertruck deliveries in 2021?

Elon Musk

All right. So we finished almost all of the Cybertrack engineering. So we're no longer iterating at the design center level or design level. We've got the designs fixed. We're getting to – we'll soon order the equipment necessary to make the Cybertruck work. We're actually going to be using even bigger Tesla machines for the rear body of Cybertruck because you've got – obviously, it's a bigger vehicle and you've got a long truck bed that's going to a lot of load.

So we'll be using an 8,000 ton casting press for the rear body casting, as opposed to 6,000 tons for Model Y. So 6,000 tons was the biggest cast in the world. 8,000 tons, quite a bit bigger than that. And I think it's going to be incredible vehicle. If we get lucky, we'll be able to do a few deliveries towards the end of this year, but I expect volume production to be in 2022.

Martin Viecha

Thank you very much. And now we can start with questions in the queue.

Operator

Thank you. Our first question will come from Colin Rusch with Oppenheimer. Please go ahead.

Colin Rusch

Thanks so much, guys. Can you talk a little bit about the regulatory environment for FSD and how you're seeing that play out? Obviously, it's a bit of a moving target right now, and you guys are really in the way here, but we'd love to understand how those conversations are going and how you see that impacting the rollout of FSD throughout the balance of this year and into next year?

Elon Musk

Okay. Zach, do you want to – I don't know, Zach and Jerome?

Zachary Kirkhorn

The – what we're seeing right now in the U.S., for example, is pretty dynamic space, but it's overall not particularly limiting on a rule basis, but what we're going to expect is to have to work with regulators to demonstrate really, really high reliability, as Elon said before.

The rest of the world is fairly dynamic. In Europe, we see a general slowdown, generally not reaching past Level 3 right now with some impetus to start working on new working groups to reach past that. And China showed an interest in working on Level 4 or even Level 5 later this year. So we expect a pretty dynamic 2021 in the regulatory space. We have leadership in the U.S. looking for manufacturers to demonstrate really good launches and really high reliability before releasing to wider and wider groups.

Colin Rusch

Thanks, guys. And then just a quick follow-up around inflation on some of the materials markets. Obviously, there's a lot going on as low interest rates flow through the basic material space. Can you talk a little bit about the supply chain and how you're migrating some of your exposure around some of your raw material costs?

Jerome Guillen

This is Jerome. Yes, for supply chain, the first priority now is to deal with the disruptions from COVID and the shipping, in particular, both between Asia and North America. But we're also looking forward to pricing, and we're watching this very closely for all the components. We are entering a series of long-term agreements with preferred suppliers to ensure that not only you're going to have enough quantity to support the growth, 50% CAGR as Zach mentioned earlier, but also good pricing with appropriate sharing of the risk.

Operator

Thank you. Our next question will come from Dan Levy with Credit Suisse. Please go ahead.

Dan Levy

Hi, good evening. Thank you. Two questions, one on 2021 and just one on capital. First, on 2021. Any expectations for what we should see on regulatory credit sales? And then the second question is on capital. Obviously, you raised a lot of capital in 2020. What should we think about the use of those funds beyond just covering some of the maturities?

And can you just give us a sense of what the elevated liquidity does and doesn't buy? Meaning, to what extent does elevated capital enable you to accelerate plans on building capacity or expanding vertical integration, accelerating timing on full self-drive features? So, those are the questions. Thank you.

Zachary Kirkhorn

Sure. On the regulatory and credit sales side, this isn't always an area that's extremely difficult for us to forecast. 2020 regulatory credit sales ended up being higher than our expectations. And it's difficult to give guidance on that. I mean what I said before is that in the long-term, regulatory credit sales will not be a material part of the business, and we don't plan the business around that. It's possible that for a handful of additional quarters, it remains strong. It's also possible that it's not.

Most of our regulatory credit revenue from Q4 was not lined up prior to the beginning of the quarter. And these were discrete deals that were struck over the course of the quarter. So, I wish I could give you more on this, Dan, but it's a space that's extraordinarily difficult for us to forecast.

On the second side, with respect to capital, a couple of things that we're thinking through there. So, as I mentioned in my opening remarks, debt reduction is an important thing that we're focused on now. Early conversions, these are things we don't have a choice on. We did around $2 billion of that in Q4.

We currently have $1.4 billion that we expect to go out in Q1 as a result of early conversions or conversions on convertible debt. That number may increase and so debt reduction is important. That's helpful on interest expense as well.

We are also using the money with respect to our investments in future capacity. And so what we're able to do now that we haven't had the opportunity to do in the past is, as we're building capacity, particularly in Austin and Berlin, we can build that capacity with the expectation of what the end state of capacity will be pulling forward some of those investments, rather than incrementally adding capacity as we go along. And so this is an important part in terms of capital efficiency that we haven't had the luxury to do in the past. And it's great to be able to have the liquidity to focus on that.

And then more broadly, as Jerome was touching on, service expansion is really important to the future strategy of the company. So, as you saw in our Q4 numbers, the expansion of service centers and mobile service from Q3 to Q4 increased quite a bit and was also quite a bit higher than the first part of the year. And so, we're able now to make investments there and also in the supercharging network to get ahead of future demand, which will cost us more in the near term, but is what the right long-term thing is for our customers and the company.

Operator

Thank you. Our next question will come from Alex Potter with Piper Sandler. Please go ahead.

Alex Potter

Great. Thanks. I was wondering, you mentioned how you'd like to increase your purchases of cells from suppliers. Does this require them to also have the capability to build structural 4680 cells of the sort that you're putting in these newer iterations of vehicles?

Elon Musk

No, it does not. Although, we are talking with them about making the 4680 form factor, but it is not required. For example, the new S currently uses the 18650 form factor. So they're just a more advanced cell, and we think we'll continue to use that form factor for at least a few years.

But we will, over time, be retiring the form factors and try to move to a consistent form factor. But it is not a requirement that we place on our suppliers, because it would just result in fewer cells. So it's better for us to deal with the complexity of different cell form factors than insist on a single form factor for our suppliers today. Like I said, over time, it will make sense to have a consistent form factor.

Alex Potter

Okay. It makes sense. And then one additional, maybe qualitative question on capacity expansion. You've mentioned in the past, I mean, access to dollars is one thing, but access to human beings that are sufficiently qualified is another. Have you run up against any issues on that front that would potentially limit your growth in any way? Thanks.

Elon Musk

That is one of the things that limits focus or limits the growth rate. It doesn't limit the ultimate size, but it limits the growth rate, which is what's the rate of which we can onboard great people and get them trained in the right areas.

You usually can't like instantaneously if you've got a factory that has 20,000 employees, you can't just hire 20,000 people instantly. They're usually doing something else. So they've got to transition from whatever they were doing or move from some other part of the country. And so there's a certain amount of time required for that.

I mean, that said, we do think that we can maintain a growth rate in excess of 50% per year for many years to come. And at least, I'd like to at least, look forward for many years to come. I think this year, we may track to a fair bit about 50%, but we don't want to commit to that, but at least that's what it would appear, and the same again next year. It appears to be meaningfully above 50%.

Operator

Thank you. Our next question will come from Joseph Spak with RBC Capital Markets. Please go ahead.

Joseph Spak

Thanks. Elon, back in 2018, you tweeted about electric vans and how it could be interesting to work with Daimler and Sprinter. We haven't really heard of anything since. But in the meantime, we've seen a lot of activity in electric van and last-mile space from a number of established players of startups. So I know you said that you have a lot of projects on the table, but can you provide us an update of your thoughts on this market? And is it something you're interested in?

Elon Musk

I think Tesla is definitely going to make an electric van at some point. The thing to bear in mind is that there is fundamentally a constraint on battery cell output. It's like if one is not involved in manufacturing, it's really hard to appreciate just how hard this to scale production is. It's the hardest thing in the world. Prototypes are easy. Scaling production is very hard.

A big part of the reason or the main reason we have not accelerated new products like, for example, Tesla Semi is that we simply don't happen is because of our cells group. If we were to make the Semi like right now, which we could easily go into production, we would not have enough cells built for it right now.

We will have cells group for Semi when producing the 4680 volume. But for example, Semi would use typically 5x the number of cells that a car would use, but it would not sell for 5x what a car would sell for. So it kind of doesn't make sense for us to do the Semi right now, but it will absolutely make sense for us to do it as soon as we can address the cell production constraint. The same would go for that.

Joseph Spak

Okay. Thank you. And then maybe if I could dig into your past on one more item. About 2 years ago, at the Autonomy Day, you stated that you're working on the next-gen Tesla chip which was about 2 years away. So is there any update on that front?

Elon Musk

Yes, to be clear, the software still does not fully use the capabilities of the FSD in 1 computer. It is really just incredibly powerful computer and I am personally certain that you can create full self-driving with safe level 5 presence just using the Full Self-Driving version 1 computer.

The version 2, we expect to be about 3x as powerful. And this needs to be paired with higher resolution cameras. And so it requires a bunch of things to change simultaneously. But we have not been rushing the version 2 of the chip. It's coming along well, and it's in good shape.

But since we can achieve FSD, Full Self-Driving, with the current system, it would actually be a distraction right now if we were to introduce the Full Self-Driving, the Tesla FSD chip 2 because it would set us back quite a bit on software. And software is the critical path to Full Self-Driving.

So I wouldn't worry too much about that. That's an improvement but not a game changer. That has to be changed. Getting the software to work and getting all the neural nets to be video, that's the game changer.

Operator

Thank you. Our next question will come from Emmanuel Rosner with Deutsche Bank. Please go ahead.

Emmanuel Rosner

Thank you very much. My first question is about your in-house cell manufacturing efforts. So in addition to building up capacity, some of the goals you highlighted was to cut the pricing or the cost by about 50%, boost the range by about 50% over a number of years. So wanted to know if your initial efforts are trending in that direction? What is, sort, of like the timeline to achieve these goals? And maybe related to this, how are you thinking about the time line for the cheaper Tesla, the entry model, eventually?

Elon Musk

I think we feel very confident about achieving those targets, let's say, over a three-year time frame. So three, maybe four years, give ourselves a little room. But for three or four years, I'd say.

Zachary Kirkhorn

Yeah. We put together the trajectory in the Battery Day, and we're on that trajectory still. I think that's probably the best reference for the cost trajectory that we are on.

Elon Musk

Yeah. We're aspiring to do better than Battery Day, but we are confident of at least for doing what we presented at Battery Day.

Operator

Thank you. Our next question will come from Ben Kallo with Baird. Please go ahead.

Ben Kallo

Hey, guys. Thank you, Elon, congrats to the whole team. So we're trying to put together all the breadcrumbs. If I remember correctly, going back 10 years, you talked about when you have a mass market car on the road, that you'd step down as CEO and be a Chief Architect. And then we have you go into Hawaii, subsea lair and the x.com, and I'm trying to put it all together. There's a lot of questions there. Thank you.

Elon Musk

Sure. Well, I expect to be CEO of Tesla for several years. So I think there's still a lot that I'm super excited about doing. And I think it would be hard to leave. I love these great projects halfway or part like hallway done. So I do expect to be running the company for several years into the future.

Now, obviously, nobody is or should be CEO forever. So I don't expect to be, like the sheer amount of work required to be CEO of Tesla is insane. And I think I do probably more, definitely do more technical work than is typical for a CEO.

So it would be nice to have a bit more free time on my hands as opposed to just working day and night, from when I wake up to when I go to sleep seven days a week, pretty intense.

I think the mission isn't over yet, and we still got a long way ago before we can really make a dent in the world on accelerating the advent of sustainable energy. I mean, the goal Tesla, from beginning, has been to accelerate sustainable energy. But if you say like what percentage of cars on the road are electric today, it's still very, very tiny, like an order of 1%, or less than 1% of the total fleet worldwide.

So that's the full have long way to go for on the order of 1% of the fleet is electric. There's also a tremendous way to go on solar power, although it's exciting to see the advent of very cost-competitive wind and solar and geothermal. And of course, we need a large volume of stationary battery packs. I mean basically, maybe the three legs of a sustainable energy future are sustainable energy generation, led by solar, wind, geothermal and hydro and a few others. And I'm actually not against nuclear fission. I actually think nuclear fission is – with a well-designed reactor in a situation that is not subject to bad weather or seriously bad weather is actually is a good thing to do.

So – and then the second thing you need is stationary storage need batteries because most renewable energy is intermittent. It doesn't – the wind doesn't blow all the time. The sun doesn't shine all the time. So you need a lot of batteries. And it needs to be very long-lasting and high cycle life. And then you need electric transport. If you have those three things, we've got a very bright future with respect to energy and the environment. So a long way to go on that. And so I'm still very much fired up to work on that.

Martin Viecha

Fantastic. And let's take the last question please.

Operator

Thank you. Our last question will come from Gene Munster with Loup Ventures. Please go ahead.

Gene Munster

I was happy to see the update on the timing of Semi and had a couple of related questions. And first, since Semi Trucks typically travel predictable highway miles, will Tesla Semi may be the first to achieve full autonomy?

Elon Musk

I think that's quite likely, yes. Yes, I can't imagine – I'm not sure who would be number two, but yes, it seems highly likely, yes.

Gene Munster

Okay. And then my...

Jerome Guillen

The hardware, it's the exact same part numbers on the Semi on the Tesla cars. There's no difference.

Elon Musk

Yes. That's true. Yes. As it is, we need to modify the parameters, software parameters change for Autopilot or Self-Driving because it needs now to Model 3, Model Y, Model X or Model S. And so this is – we just need to inform the vehicle, inform the Full Self-Driving brain that it is now in a Semi Truck.

Gene Munster

Would it need to be retrained then as part of that?

Elon Musk

No. I think there will be – you have a different control functions because there are turns that you could do in a regular car that you cannot do in a Semi, like you do want to try to parallel park this thing on the street in a city. It needs to know its limitations being a giant truck.

Gene Munster

Makes sense. My follow-up question was related to if you could just help us explain why battery electric will win versus hydrogen cell fuel tech?

Elon Musk

Yes. I mean, honestly, I've had this question a million times for just for regular vehicles, even back in the early Roadster days, even before we had the Roadster out. People were saying that somehow hydrogen is going to be a better means of energy storage in a car than batteries. And it was like this is just really not the case.

Hydrogen is a very – it's number one in the periodic table. It's got very low density. It's got low density as a liquid, like styrofoam-level density as a liquid. And then it's only a liquid very close to absolute zero. it's really not realistic to keep it as liquid.

You want to have it as a high-pressure gas that has even lower density. So you need a gigantic fuel tank volumetrically, and it's got to be very high pressure. It's a big pain yes, basically. If somebody is going to say, use an ultimate chemical energy storage mechanism to hydrogen, I'd say just use propane or something like that, or methane, those will be way better than hydrogen. And then having it be a fuel cell just adds even further complications to the situation. It's just crazy basically.

And we're extremely confident that we could make a long-range trucking with batteries. The math works out. If you could just like take, say, watt-hours per kilogram of currently available cells, and say, okay, how much weight would you need to go, let's say, 500 miles? And to what degree does that affect your payload? And it's like, okay, do this. If you do it right, you basically have no effect on your payload or almost nothing, and you can have a long-range truck. I mean, Jerome, do you want to add to that?

Jerome Guillen

I agree there. And we see also an increase on the regionalization of trucks. And I think it will be perfect. The Tesla Semi will be perfect for it, yes. And I'm looking forward to having some additional ones on the road very soon.

Elon Musk

But basically, we do not see any issues with creating a compelling long-range truck with batteries. The problem is cell supply; cell supply is the only thing.

Gene Munster

It's going to be awesome.

Elon Musk

Yes.

Martin Viecha

All right. Thank you very much. And unfortunately, that's all the time we have today. So, thanks for all of your great questions, and we will speak to you again in about three months. Thank you.

Elon Musk

Thanks so much. Bye.

Operator

Ladies and gentlemen, this concludes today's conference call. Thank you for your participation. You may now disconnec

Companies

These are the ventures where Elon Musk is presently involved.

Tesla. Automotive - Electric self-driving cars.

Tesla was founded in 2003 to prove that electric vehicles can be better, quicker and more fun to drive than gasoline cars. Today, Tesla builds not only all-electric vehicles but also infinitely scalable clean energy generation and storage products. Tesla believes the faster the world stops relying on fossil fuels and moves towards a zero-emission future, the better.

SpaceX. Aerospace

First commercial company to send NASA astronauts to the International Space Station and back. SpaceX goal is also to make humanity multiplanetary.

SpaceX is working on a next generation of fully reusable launch vehicles that will be the most powerful ever built, capable of carrying humans to Mars and other destinations in the solar system.

SpaceX believes a fully and rapidly reusable rocket is the pivotal breakthrough needed to substantially reduce the cost of space access. The majority of the launch cost comes from building the rocket, which historically has flown only once.

Neuralink. Brain interface

The Future of Neural Engineering - The Link is a starting point for a new kind of brain interface. These brain Implants are chip of electrodes that are surgically implanted directly into the brain to cure neurological diseases or injuries as strokes, neurodegeneration, cancer, spinal cord injuries, amputations and other healthcare issues.

This technology will be able to increase the channels of communication with the brain, accessing more brain areas and new kinds of neural information.

Solarcity. Solar energy

SolarCity is the #1 provider of residential and commercial solar. It maintains a vertically integrated supply chain for high efficiency module manufacturing.

Tesla solar panels are designed to be highly efficient, delivering maximum solar production year-round, even on roofs with complicated angles.

The Boring Company. Transportation

The Boring Company creates safe, fast-to-dig, and low-cost transportation, utility, and freight tunnels.

The mission: solve traffic, enable rapid point-to-point transportation and transform cities

Loop is an express public transportation system that resembles an underground highway more than a subway system.

Hyperloop. Transportation

Hyperloop is a new mode of transport it consists of a low pressure tube with capsules that are transported at both low and high speeds throughout the length of the tube. The capsules are accelerated via a magnetic linear accelerator affixed at various stations on the low pressure tube with rotors contained in each capsule.

Starlink. Telecommunications

Starlink is a satellite internet constellation being constructed by SpaceX providing satellite Internet access. The constellation will consist of thousands of mass-produced small satellites in low Earth orbit, which communicate with designated ground transceivers.

OPENAI. Artificial intelligence

OpenAI is an AI research and deployment company. Its mission is to ensure that artificial general intelligence benefits all of humanity.

A more complete portrayal of each of these companies, as described on their respective sites, can be found in the next chapters.

Tesla

Tesla's mission is to accelerate the world's transition to sustainable energy.

Tesla was founded in 2003 by a group of engineers who wanted to prove that people didn't need to compromise to drive electric – that electric vehicles can be better, quicker and more fun to drive than gasoline cars. Today, Tesla builds not only all-electric vehicles but also infinitely scalable clean energy generation and storage products. Tesla believes the faster the world stops relying on fossil fuels and moves towards a zero-emission future, the better.

Launched in 2008, the Roadster unveiled Tesla's cutting-edge battery technology and electric powertrain. From there, Tesla designed the world's first ever premium all-electric sedan from the ground up – Model S – which has become the best car in its class in every category. Combining safety, performance, and efficiency, Model S has reset the world's expectations for the car of the 21st century with the longest range of any electric vehicle, over-the-air software updates that make it better over time, and a record 0-60 mph acceleration time of 2.28 seconds as measured by Motor Trend. In 2015, Tesla expanded its product line with Model X, the safest, quickest and most capable sport utility vehicle in history that holds 5-star safety ratings across every category from the National Highway Traffic Safety Administration.

Completing CEO Elon Musk's "Secret Master Plan," in 2016, Tesla introduced Model 3, a low-priced, high-volume electric vehicle that began production in 2017. Soon after, Tesla unveiled the safest, most comfortable truck ever – Tesla Semi – which is designed to save owners at least $200,000 over a million miles based on fuel costs alone. In 2019, Tesla unveiled Model Y, a mid-size SUV, with seating for up to seven, and Cybertruck, which will have better utility than a traditional truck and more performance than a sports car.

Tesla vehicles are produced at its factory in Fremont, California, and Gigafactory Shanghai. To achieve our goal of having the safest factories in the world, Tesla is taking a proactive approach to safety, requiring production employees to participate in a multi-day training program before ever setting foot on the factory floor. From there, Tesla continues to provide on-the-job training and track performance daily so that improvements can be made quickly. The result is that Tesla's safety rate continues to improve while production ramps.

To create an entire sustainable energy ecosystem, Tesla also manufactures a unique set of energy solutions, Powerwall, Powerpack and Solar Roof, enabling homeowners, businesses, and utilities to manage renewable energy generation, storage, and consumption. Supporting Tesla's automotive and energy products is Gigafactory 1 – a facility designed to significantly reduce battery cell costs. By bringing cell production in-house, Tesla manufactures batteries at the volumes required to meet production goals, while creating thousands of jobs.

And this is just the beginning. With Tesla building its most affordable car yet, Tesla continues to make products accessible and affordable to more and more people, ultimately accelerating the advent of clean transport and clean energy production. Electric cars, batteries, and renewable energy generation and storage already exist independently, but when combined, they become even more powerful – that's the future we want.

Latest News from Tesla – January, 2021

Model Y Achieves 5-Star Overall Safety Rating from NHTSA.

Since the launch of Model S in 2012, we have engineered every Tesla around the same advanced architecture that maximizes occupant safety. Today, Model Y, Tesla's mid-size Sport Utility Vehicle (SUV), is the latest Tesla vehicle to earn a 5-star safety rating in every category from the National Highway Traffic Safety Administration (NHTSA).

As part of their 2020 New Car Assessment Program, NHTSA tested Model Y Long Range All-Wheel Drive (AWD). We expect similar results for all Model Y variants, including our Performance AWD and single motor, rear-wheel drive variants in the future.

What makes Model Y safe?

Model 3 and Model Y were developed largely on the same platform, and this shared architecture is fundamental to both vehicles' safety. To accommodate its higher mass and larger cabin space as an SUV, Model Y's body structure is fortified and strengthened even further than Model 3 in pursuit of its 5-star safety rating.

At its core, in the event of a collision, Model Y is engineered to distribute crash forces around the cabin and away from vehicle occupants, greatly reducing the risk of injury. Our front and rear crumple zones and optimized side structures enable Model Y to manage crash energy very efficiently, reducing accelerations on the vehicle and, more critically, its occupants.

Additionally, Model Y's structure now includes the world's largest casting. Along with a fortified battery pack, these elements mitigate intrusion into the cabin, creating a robust safety cell with enough room for our advanced restraint systems to deploy and provide even more occupant protection.

Rollover risk

Rollovers significantly increase the risk of injury during an accident. To calculate rollover resistance in NHTSA's test, Model Y is parked on a suspended platform that rotates in all directions to physically measure center of gravity and moments of inertia. NHTSA's assessment determined that Model Y has a rollover risk of 7.9%, the lowest of any SUV recorded to date by the organization.

As with all Tesla vehicles, Model Y's architecture is fundamentally designed to have a very low center of gravity, which is accomplished by strategically placing its heavy battery pack and electric motors low down in the vehicle. Safety is at the core of every Tesla vehicle, and Model Y benefits from years of immense passion for vehicle safety. Every Tesla comes standard with advanced crash-avoidance and pedestrian protection features, including Automatic Emergency Braking, Lane Departure Warning and Forward Collision Warning, among others. By providing the most advanced equipment and technologies, our goal is to help customers prevent avoidable accidents whenever possible, and, when they are not avoidable, to help mitigate injury to the fullest extent possible. Indeed, we believe Model Y to be among the safest vehicles available to consumers on the road.

Sales of Tesla vehicles worldwide

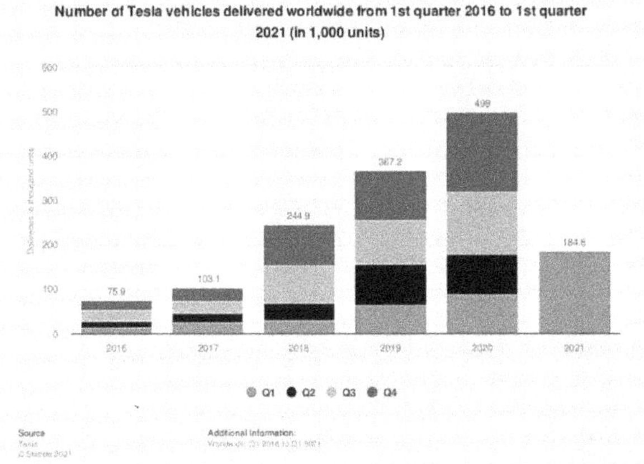

SpaceX

MAKING HUMANITY MULTIPLANETARY

Building on the achievements of Falcon 9 and Falcon Heavy, SpaceX is working on a next generation of fully reusable launch vehicles that will be the most powerful ever built, capable of carrying humans to Mars and other destinations in the solar system.

MAKING HISTORY

SpaceX has gained worldwide attention for a series of historic milestones. It is the only private company capable of returning a spacecraft from low-Earth orbit, and in 2012 our Dragon spacecraft became the first commercial spacecraft to deliver cargo to and from the International Space Station. And in 2020, SpaceX became the first private company to take humans there as well. Click through the timeline above to see some of our milestone accomplishments.

REUSABILITY

SpaceX believes a fully and rapidly reusable rocket is the pivotal breakthrough needed to substantially reduce the cost of space access. The majority of the launch cost comes from building the rocket, which historically has flown only once.

Compare that to a commercial airliner – each new plane costs about the same as Falcon 9 but can fly multiple times per day and conduct tens of thousands of flights over its lifetime. Following the commercial model, a rapidly reusable space launch vehicle could reduce the cost of traveling to space by a hundredfold.

While most rockets are designed to burn up on reentry, SpaceX rockets can not only withstand reentry but can also successfully land back on Earth and refly again.

LANDING

SpaceX's family of Falcon launch vehicles are the first and only orbital class rockets capable of reflight. Depending on the performance required for the mission, Falcon lands on one of our autonomous spaceport droneships out on the ocean or one of our landing zones near our launch pads.

SPACEX FACILITIES

CALIFORNIA - BUILD FACILITY

SpaceX designs and builds its reusable rockets and spacecraft at its headquarters in Hawthorne, California. As a company, SpaceX is vertically integrated, building the vast majority of the vehicle on the Hawthorne campus. SpaceX headquarters remains one of the few facilities in the world where you can see an entire launch vehicle or spacecraft come together under one roof.

TEXAS - TESTING FACILITY

SpaceX tests its engines, vehicle structures, and systems at a 4,000-acre state-of-the-art rocket development facility in McGregor, Texas. Outfitted with 16 specialized test stands, the facility validates for flight every Merlin engine that powers the Falcon 9 and Falcon Heavy rockets, and every Draco thruster that controls the Dragon spacecraft.

FLORIDA - CAPE CANAVERAL SPACE FORCE STATION, SPACE LAUNCH COMPLEX 40

The site's location on the southeast coast of the US provides access to a wide range of low and medium inclination orbits frequently used by communications and Earth-observing satellites and by supply missions to the International Space Station. The site also allows access to geostationary orbits, as well as departures to the Moon and interplanetary destinations.

FLORIDA - KENNEDY SPACE CENTER, LAUNCH COMPLEX 39A

SpaceX is honored to launch from Kennedy Space Center's historic Launch Complex 39A, home of the Apollo and Space Shuttle programs. In addition to commercial satellite launches and space station resupply missions, LC-39A supports crew launches of the Dragon spacecraft.

CALIFORNIA -VANDENBERG AIR FORCE BASE, SPACE LAUNCH COMPLEX 4 EAST

The site's location on the California coastline provides customers with access to high inclination and polar orbits, frequently used by satellite communication constellations, defense intelligence and Earth-observing satellites, and some lunar missions. Launches from Vandenberg heading straight south traverse open ocean all the way to the Antarctic, by which time the vehicles have long since reached orbit.

TEXAS - STARBASE

SpaceX is building the world's first commercial launch site designed for orbital missions at Starbase in Texas. Starbase is where build and test development for Starship vehicles takes place.

Neuralink

Breakthrough Technology for the Brain

Interfacing with the Brain

Innovation pushing the boundaries of neural engineering.

Expanding Our World - A team of exceptionally talented people. We are creating the future of brain interfaces: building devices now that will help people with paralysis and inventing new technologies that will expand our abilities, our community, and our world.

FROM NEURON TO COMPUTER

A Direct Link Between the Brain & Everyday Technology

The initial goal of our technology will be to help people with paralysis to regain independence through the control of computers and mobile devices. Our devices are designed to give people the ability to communicate more easily via text or speech synthesis, to follow their curiosity on the web, or to express their creativity through photography, art, or writing apps.

The Future of Neural Engineering - The Link is a starting point for a new kind of brain interface. As our technology develops, we will be able to increase the channels of communication with the brain, accessing more brain areas and new kinds of neural information. This technology has the potential to treat a wide range of neurological disorders, to restore sensory and movement function, and eventually to expand how we interact with each other, with the world, and with ourselves.

We are designing the first neural implant that will let you control a computer or mobile device anywhere you go. Micron-scale threads are inserted into areas of the brain that control movement. Each thread contains many electrodes and connects them to an implant, the Link.

LINK

Sealed, implanted device that processes, stimulates, and transmits neural signals.

NEURAL THREADS

Each small and flexible thread contains many electrodes for detecting neural signals.

CHARGER

Compact inductive charger wirelessly connects to the implant to charge the battery from the outside.

Precision Automated Neurosurgery

The threads on the Link are so fine and flexible that they can't be inserted by the human hand. Instead, we are building a robotic system that the neurosurgeon can use to reliably and efficiently insert these threads exactly where they need to be.

The Neuralink App

The Neuralink app would allow you to control your iOS device, keyboard and mouse directly with the activity of your brain, just by thinking about it.

BE IN CONTROL

The Neuralink app would guide you through exercises that teach you to control your device.

BE AUTONOMOUS

With a bluetooth connection, you would control any mouse or keyboard, and experience reality — unmediated and in high fidelity.

WHAT WILL THE LINK DO?

We are designing the Link to connect to thousands of neurons in the brain. It will be able to record the activity of these neurons, process these signals in real time, and send that information to the Link. As a first application of this technology, we plan to help people with severe spinal cord injury by giving them the ability to control computers and mobile devices directly with their brains. We would start by recording neural activity in the brain's movement areas. As users think about moving their arms or hands, we would decode those intentions, which would be sent over Bluetooth to the user's computer. Users would initially learn to control a virtual mouse. Later, as users get more practice and our adaptive decoding algorithms continue to improve, we expect that users would be able to control multiple devices, including a keyboard or a game controller.

WHO WILL THE LINK HELP?

We expect our first application to be computer control for people with spinal cord injury. There are many other potential future applications for the Link. These include restoring motor and sensory function and the treatment of neurological disorders.

WILL THE LINK BE SAFE?

We have not yet begun clinical trials, and so we do not have safety data in humans. But safety has been at the core of the design process. In particular, the Link includes technical innovations for improving the safety of the surgical procedure compared to existing BMI devices or traditional neurosurgery. Here are a few examples.

There is always risk associated with general anesthesia, and that risk is reduced by shortening the time of the procedure. The Neurosurgical Robot is capable of efficient and reliable electrode insertion. Also, the robot is being designed to insert threads through a hole in the skull as small as 23 mm diameter. Combined with other advancements in robotic surgical tooling, this may allow us to eliminate general

anesthesia and to implant the device under conscious sedation.
Inserting a device into the brain always carries some risk of bleeding. We are trying to reduce that risk by using micron-scale threads, inserted with a needle whose diameter is about the size of many neurons in the brain. Furthermore, because each thread is individually inserted, we are designing the Neurosurgical Robot to avoid damaging blood vessels at or near the surface of the brain.

WILL THE LINK OR FUTURE SYSTEMS BE AVAILABLE TO HEALTHY PEOPLE?

Neuralink is currently focused on making medical devices. These devices have the potential to help people with a wide range of injuries and neurological disorders, and we hope to develop treatments for many of these conditions in the coming years. We expect that as our devices continue scale, and as we learn to communicate with more areas of the brain, we will discover new, non-medical applications for our BMIs. Neuralink's long-term vision is to create BMIs that are sufficiently safe and powerful that healthy individuals would want to have them.

HOW WILL YOU ADDRESS DEVICE SECURITY?

We understand that medical devices need to be secure, and it takes serious engineering to prevent unwanted access to such devices. Security will be built into every layer of the product, using strong cryptography, defensive engineering, and extensive security auditing.

WHAT IS NEURALINK DEVELOPING?

Neuralink is building a fully integrated brain machine interface (BMI) system. Sometimes you'll see this called a brain computer interface (BCI). Either way, BMIs are technologies that enable a computer or other digital device to communicate directly with the brain. For example, through information readout from the brain, a person with paralysis can control a computer mouse or keyboard. Or, information can be written back into the brain, for example to restore the sense of touch. Our goal is to build a system with at least two orders of magnitude more communication channels (electrodes) than current clinically-approved devices. This system needs to be safe, it must have fully wireless communication through the skin, and it has to be ready for patients to take home and use on their own. Our device, called the Link, will be able to record from 1024 electrodes and is designed to meet these criteria.

WHAT ARE THE BIGGEST CHALLENGES IN MAKING A SCALABLE BMI?

Neuralink's technology builds on decades of BMI research in academic labs, including several ongoing studies with human participants. The BMI systems used in these studies have no more than a few hundred electrodes, with connectors that pass through the skin. Also, their use requires laboratory equipment and personnel. Our challenge is to scale up the number of electrodes while also building a safe and effective clinical system that users can take home and operate by themselves. Recent engineering advances in the field and new technologies developed at Neuralink are paving the way for progress on each of the key technical hurdles.

ELECTRODES

In order to optimize the compatibility of our threads with the surrounding tissue, they should be on the same size scale as neighboring neurons and as flexible as possible. Therefore, we microfabricate the threads out of thin film metals and polymers. But the threads also have to resist corrosion from fluid in the tissue, and the electrodes must have sufficient surface area to allow stimulation. To meet these criteria, we've developed new microfabrication processes and made advances in materials science. These include the integration of corrosion-resistant adhesion layers to the threads and rough electrode materials that increase their effective surface area without increasing their size.

CHIPS

Our Link needs to convert the small electrical signals recorded by each electrode into real-time neural information. Since the neural signals in the brain are small (microvolts), Link must have high-performance signal amplifiers and digitizers. Also, as the number of electrodes increases, these raw digital signals become too much information to upload with low power devices. So scaling our devices requires on-chip, real-time identification and characterization of neural spikes. Our custom chips on the Link meet these goals, while radically reducing per-channel chip size and power consumption over current technology.

HERMETIC PACKAGING

The Link needs to be protected from the fluid and salts that bathe surrounding tissue. Making a water-proof enclosure can be hard, but it's very hard when that enclosure must be constructed from biocompatible materials, replace the skull structurally, and allow over a 1,000 electrical channels to pass through it. To meet this challenge, we are developing innovative techniques to build and seal each major component of the package.

For example, by replacing the connection of multiple components with a process that builds them as a single component, we can decrease device size and eliminate a potential failure point.

NEUROSURGERY

Our threads are too fine to be manipulated by hand and too flexible to go into the brain on their own (imagine trying to sew a button with thread but no needle). Yet we need to safely insert them with precision and efficiency. Our solution is based on a new kind of surgical robot, whose initial prototype was developed at the University of California. We are innovating on robot design, imaging systems, and software, to build a robot that can precisely and efficiently insert many threads through a single 8 mm skull opening while avoiding blood vessels on the surface of the brain.

NEURAL-DECODING

Neural spikes contain a lot of information, but that information has to be decoded in order to use it for controlling a computer. Academic labs have designed computer algorithms controlling a virtual computer mouse from the activity of hundreds of neurons. Our devices will be able to connect to over an order of magnitude more neurons. We want to use the additional information for more precise and naturalistic control and to include additional virtual devices such as a keyboard and game controller. To accomplish this, we are building on recent advances in statistics and algorithm design. One challenge is to design adaptive algorithms that maintain reliable and robust performance while continuing to improve over time, including the addition of new capabilities. Ultimately, we want these algorithms to run in real time on our low-power devices.

HOW DOES THE NEURALINK SYSTEM DIFFER FROM OTHER BMI DEVICES?

There are currently only a few approved devices for recording or stimulating from the human brain, including devices for deep brain stimulation (DBS), which can treat neurological disorders such as Parkinson's Disease, and devices for the detection and disruption of seizures. These are designed to modulate the activity of whole brain areas, not to transfer information to and from the brain. Therefore, they only have a small number of electrodes (less than 10) and are much larger than our threads. For example, DBS leads have only 4-8 electrodes and are about 800 times larger.

There are other devices being used in clinical trials for BMI movement control or sensory restoration. However, none of these devices have more than a few hundred electrodes, and they are all either placed on the surface of the brain or in fixed arrays of single rigid electrodes. The Link is being designed with an order of magnitude more electrodes and with flexible threads that are individually placed to avoid blood vessels and to best cover the brain region of interest.

We are also designing the Link to provide unprecedented scale, with over 1024 channels of information from the brain. The Link will also perform real-time spike detection on every channel, and these data will all be sent wirelessly.

HOW DOES THE NEURALINK SYSTEM DIFFER FROM OTHER BMI DEVICES?

There are currently only a few approved devices for recording or stimulating from the human brain, including devices for deep brain stimulation (DBS), which can treat neurological disorders such as Parkinson's Disease, and devices for the detection and disruption of seizures. These are designed to modulate the activity of whole brain areas, not to transfer information to and from the brain. Therefore, they only have a small number of electrodes (less than 10) and are much larger than our threads.

For example, DBS leads have only 4-8 electrodes and are about 800 times larger.

There are other devices being used in clinical trials for BMI movement control or sensory restoration. However, none of these devices have more than a few hundred electrodes, and they are all either placed on the surface of the brain or in fixed arrays of single rigid electrodes. The Link is being designed with an order of magnitude more electrodes and with flexible threads that are individually placed to avoid blood vessels and to best cover the brain region of interest.

We are also designing the Link to provide unprecedented scale, with over 1024 channels of information from the brain. The Link will also perform real-time spike detection on every channel, and these data will all be sent wirelessly.

The Boring Company

The Boring Company creates safe, fast-to-dig, and low-cost transportation, utility, and freight tunnels.

The mission: solve traffic, enable rapid point-to-point transportation and transform cities

INTRODUCING LOOP

Loop is an all-electric, zero-emissions, underground public transportation system in which passengers are transported directly to their final destination with no stops along the way.

Located at the Las Vegas Convention Center, LVCC Loop is the first commercially operating Loop system.

DISTINCTION FROM SUBWAY

Loop is an express public transportation system that resembles an underground highway more than a subway system.

If a subway line had 100 stops, a train would typically stop at each station, so the trip between Stop 1 and Stop 100 would be long. In contrast, Loop passengers travel directly to their destination, anywhere between Stop 1 to Stop 100, without stopping at the intermediate stations. Also, the express system allow Loop vehicles to travel faster than conventional subway cars (up to 150 mph vs. up to 65 mp

CAPACITY

Loop passenger capacity is a function of the quantity of tunnels, quantity of stations, the size of stations, and the quantity of operating vehicles. The LVCC Loop system is designed for 4,400 passengers per hour (with 3 large stations), while Vegas Loop is targeting 51,000 passengers per hour (with 43 medium-sized stations).

UNCONGESTED ENTRY AND EXIT

Unlike a subway, there is no practical upper limit to the number of stations that can be built along the tunnel route because stations can be as small as two parking spaces. Since stations require such a small footprint, they can easily be integrated in busy city centers, parking garages, and residential communities. This high density of stations will distribute AEV and foot traffic across many access points, providing more convenient entry and exit locations and reducing congestion in populated areas. If needed, larger stations can be built to increase capacity.

WHY TUNNELS?

Solve traffic: to solve the problem of soul-destroying traffic, roads must go 3D. Surface roads today incorporate 3D model-like elevated highways and cloverleaf interchanges that are expensive and disruptive to build. Tunneling networks are 3D and provide high-throughput transportation in an economically viable way. Traffic and congestion will be a thing of the past.

Beautify our cities: existing transportation networks occupy valuable space in cities where land availability is scarce. Tunnels minimize usage of surface area and could move entire transportation networks underground. Taking transportation underground allows us to repurpose roads into community-enhancing spaces, and beautify our cities.

Enable Hyperloop: Hyperloop networks unlock high-speed regional transportation surpassing other alternatives. Hyperloop enables access to individualized, point to point high-speed transportation.

THE BENEFITS OF TUNNELS

Unlimited Capacity: there is no practical limit to how many layers of tunnels can be built, so any current or future capacity outcome can be achieved. This flexibility contrasts with a surface system where adding a lane to the road is often difficult

Minimal Use of Land: tunnels minimize the use of valuable surface land. Tunnels also do not conflict with currently operating transportation systems, such as roads and sidewalks

Weatherproof Operation: rain, snow, wind, and surface temperatures do not affect system operation

Minimal Surface Impact: tunnel construction and operation do not create any discernible surface noise or vibration. Tunnel construction and operation are invisible, silent, and undetectable

Future Expansion: it is much simpler to extend a tunnel-based system than a surface-based system

Currently, tunnels are really expensive to dig, with many projects costing between $100 million and $1 billion per mile. In order to make vast tunnel networks feasible, tunneling costs must be reduced by a factor of more than 10, with TBC's Loop tunnels currently priced at approximately $10 million per mile

CONSTRUCTION

Utilities: with a typical minimum depth of 30 feet, our tunnels are well beneath most utilities, which are typically less than 10 feet below the surface. In circumstances where a utility is located deeper, the tunnel depth is increased accordingly

No disruptive surface vibration or noise during tunneling: once a tunnel boring machine is below approximately two tunnel diameters, or 28 feet, the tunneling process is almost impossible to detect, especially in soft soil. The tunnel operation is inaudible, and there is typically more surface vibration felt from a pedestrian walking nearby than from the TBM operating 30+ feet below

Managing excavated dirt: in typical tunneling projects, excavated dirt is shipped offsite to disposal locations. This process is costly, time-consuming, noisy, and environmentally-unsustainable. We recycle a portion of the muck into useful bricks and pavers to be used to build anything from affordable housing to patios. This is not a new concept, as buildings have been constructed from earth for thousands of years including, according to recent evidence, the Pyramids. These earth blocks can potentially be used as a portion of the tunnel lining itself, which is typically built from concrete. Since concrete production accounts for 4.5% of the world's greenhouse gas emissions, earth blocks would reduce both environmental impact and tunneling costs

Hyperloop

Existing conventional modes of transportation of people consists of four unique types: rail, road, water, and air. These modes of transport tend to be either relatively slow (e.g., road and water), expensive (e.g., air), or a combination of relatively slow and expensive (i.e., rail). Hyperloop is a new mode of transport that seeks to change this paradigm by being both fast and inexpensive for people and goods. Hyperloop is also unique in that it is an open design concept, similar to Linux. Feedback is desired from the community that can help advance the Hyperloop design and bring it from concept to reality.

Hyperloop consists of a low pressure tube with capsules that are transported at both low and high speeds throughout the length of the tube. The capsules are supported on a cushion of air, featuring pressurized air and aerodynamic lift. The capsules are accelerated via a magnetic linear accelerator affixed at various stations on the low pressure tube with rotors contained in each capsule. Passengers may enter and exit Hyperloop at stations located either at the ends of the tube, or branches along the tube length.

In this study, the initial route, preliminary design, and logistics of the Hyperloop transportation system have been derived. The system consists of capsules that travel between Los Angeles, California and San Francisco, California. The total one-way trip time is 35 minutes from county line to county line. The capsules leave on average every 2 minutes from each terminal carrying 28 people each (as often as every 30 seconds during rush hour and less frequently at night).

This gives a total of 7.4 million people per tube that can be transported each year on Hyperloop. The total cost of Hyperloop is under $6 billion USD for two one-way tubes and 40 capsules. Amortizing this capital cost over 20 years and adding daily operational costs gives a total of $20 USD plus operating costs per one-way ticket on the passenger Hyperloop.

BACKROUND

The corridor between San Francisco, California and Los Angeles, California is one of the most often traveled corridors in the American West. The current practical modes of transport for passengers between these two major population centers include:

1. Road (inexpensive, slow, usually not environmentally sound)

2. Air (expensive, fast, not environmentally sound)

3. Rail (expensive, slow, often environmentally sound)

A new mode of transport is needed that has benefits of the current modes without the negative aspects of each. This new high speed transportation system has the following requirements:

1. Ready when the passenger is ready to travel (road)
2.Inexpensive-(road)
3.Fast-(air)
4. Environmentally friendly (rail/road via electric cars)

The current contender for a new transportation system between southern and northern California is the "California High Speed Rail." The parameters outlining this system include:

Currently $68.4 billion USD proposed cost

Average speed of 164 mph (264 kph) between San Francisco and Los Angeles

The Travel time of 2 hours and 38 minutes between San Francisco and Los Angeles

a. Compare with 1 hour and 15 minutes by air
b. Compare with 5 hours and 30 minutes by car

Average one-way ticket price of $105 one-way

Compare with $158 round trip by air for September 2013

Compare with $115 round trip by road ($4/gallon with 30 mpg vehicle)

A new high speed mode of transport is desired between Los Angeles and San Francisco; however, the proposed California High Speed Rail does not reduce current trip times or reduce costs relative to existing modes of transport. This preliminary design study proposes a new mode of high speed transport that reduces both the travel time and travel cost between Los Angeles and San Francisco. Options are also included to increase the transportation system to other major population centers across California. It is also worth noting the energy cost of this system is less than any currently existing mode of transport (Figure 1). The only system that comes close to matching the low energy requirements of Hyperloop is the fully electric Tesla Model S.

Hyperloop Transportation System

Hyperloop is a proposed transportation system for traveling between Los Angeles, California, and San Francisco, California in 35 minutes. The Hyperloop consists of several distinct components, including:

1. Capsule:

Sealed capsules carrying 28 passengers each that travel along the

interior of the tube depart on average every 2 minutes from Los Angeles or San Francisco (up to every 30 seconds during peak usage hours).

A larger system has also been sized that allows transport of 3 full size automobiles with passengers to travel in the capsule.

The capsules are separated within the tube by approximately 23 miles (37 km) on average during operation.

The capsules are supported via air bearings that operate using a compressed air reservoir and aerodynamic lift.

2. Tube:

The tube is made of steel. Two tubes will be welded together in a

side-by-side configuration to allow the capsules to travel both directions.

Pylons are placed every 100 ft (30 m) to support the tube.

Solar arrays will cover the top of the tubes in order to provide

power to the system.

3. Propulsion:

Linear accelerators are constructed along the length of the tube at various locations to accelerate the capsules.

Rotors are located on the capsules to transfer momentum to the capsules via the linear accelerators.

4. Route:

There will be a station at Los Angeles and San Francisco. Several

stations along the way will be possible with splits in the tube.

The majority of the route will follow I-5 and the tube will be constructed in the median.

Capsule

Two versions of the Hyperloop capsules are being considered: a passenger only version and a passenger plus vehicle version.

Hyperloop Passenger Capsule

Assuming an average departure time of 2 minutes between capsules, a minimum of 28 passengers per capsule are required to meet 840 passengers per hour. It is possible to further increase the Hyperloop capacity by reducing the time between departures. The current baseline requires up to 40 capsules in activity during rush hour, 6 of which are at the terminals for loading and unloading of the passengers in approximately 5 minutes.

Hyperloop Passenger Plus Vehicle Capsule

The passenger plus vehicle version of the Hyperloop will depart as often as the passenger only version, but will accommodate 3 vehicles in addition to the passengers. All subsystems discussed in the following sections are featured on both capsules.

For travel at high speeds, the greatest power requirement is normally to overcome air resistance. Aerodynamic drag increases with the square of speed, and thus the power requirement increases with the cube of speed. For example, to travel twice as fast a vehicle must overcome four times the aerodynamic resistance, and input eight times the power.

Just as aircraft climb to high altitudes to travel through less dense air, Hyperloop encloses the capsules in a reduced pressure tube. The pressure of air in Hyperloop is about 1/6 the pressure of the atmosphere on Mars. This is an operating pressure of 100 Pascals, which reduces the drag force of the air by 1,000 times relative to sea level conditions and would be equivalent to flying above 150,000 feet altitude. A hard vacuum is avoided as vacuums are expensive and difficult to maintain compared with low pressure solutions. Despite the low pressure, aerodynamic challenges must still be addressed. These include managing the formation of shock waves when the speed of the capsule approaches the speed of sound, and the air resistance increases sharply. Close to the cities where more turns must be navigated, capsules travel at a lower speed. This reduces the accelerations felt by the passengers, and also reduces power requirements for the capsule. The capsules travel at 760 mph (1,220 kph, Mach 0.99 at 68 oF or 20 oC).

The vehicle is streamlined to reduce drag and features a compressor at the leading face to ingest oncoming air for levitation and to a lesser extent propulsion. Aerodynamic simulations have demonstrated the validity of this 'compressor within a tube' concept (Figure 7).

Hyperloop Passenger Capsule

The maximum width is 4.43 ft (1.35 m) and maximum height is 3.61 ft (1.10 m). With rounded corners, this is equivalent to a 15 ft^2 (1.4 m^2) frontal area, not including any propulsion or suspension components.

The aerodynamic power requirements at 700 mph (1,130 kph) is around only 134 hp (100 kW) with a drag force of only 72 lb_f (320 N), or about the same force as the weight of one oversized checked bag at the airport. The doors on each side will open in a gullwing (or possibly sliding) manner to allow easy access during loading and unloading. The luggage compartment will be at the front or rear of the capsule.

The overall structure weight is expected to be near 6,800 lb (3,100 kg) including the luggage compartments and door mechanism. The overall cost of the structure including manufacturing is targeted to be no more than $245,000.

Hyperloop Passenger Plus Vehicle Capsule

The passenger plus vehicle version of the Hyperloop capsule has an increased frontal area of 43 ft^2 (4.0 m^2), not including any propulsion or suspension components. This accounts for enough width to fit a vehicle as large as the Tesla Model X.

The aerodynamic power requirement at 700 mph (1,130 kph) is around only 382 hp (285 kW) with a drag force of 205 lbf (910 N). The doors on each side will open in a gullwing (or possibly sliding) manner to accommodate loading of vehicles, passengers, or freight.

The overall structure weight is expected to be near 7,700 lb (3,500 kg) including the luggage compartments and door mechanism. The overall cost of the structure including manufacturing is targeted to be no more than $275,000.

The interior of the capsule is specifically designed with passenger safety and comfort in mind. The seats conform well to the body to maintain comfort during the high speed accelerations experienced during travel. Beautiful landscape will be displayed in the cabin and each passenger will have access their own personal entertainment system.

Hyperloop Passenger Capsule

The Hyperloop passenger capsule overall interior weight is expected to be near 5,500 lb (2,500 kg) including the seats, restraint systems, interior and door panels, luggage compartments, and entertainment.

Hyperloop is considered an open source transportation concept. The authors encourage all members of the community to contribute to the Hyperloop design process. Iteration of the design by various individuals and groups can help bring Hyperloop from an idea to a reality.

The authors recognize the need for additional work, including but not limited to:

More expansion on the control mechanism for Hyperloop capsules, including attitude thruster or control moment gyros.

Detailed station designs with loading and unloading of both passenger and passenger plus vehicle versions of the Hyperloop capsules.

Trades comparing the costs and benefits of Hyperloop with more conventional magnetic levitation systems.

Sub-scale testing based on a further optimized design to demonstrate the physics of Hyperloop.

Feedback is welcomed on these or any useful aspects of the Hyperloop design.

E-mail feedback to hyperloop@spacex.com

SolarCity

Tesla and SolarCity

Our Mission, our Vision, and our Products

Record High CO_2Levels

This year, CO_2concentration levels permanently exceeded the alarming 400 parts per million threshold. Many climate scientists believe this level will have a catastrophic impact on the environment. According to NASA, 2016 had the warmest September in 136 years of modern record-keeping.

Tesla's mission has always been to help solve this problem by accelerating the world's transition to sustainable energy. To achieve this, energy needs to be sustainably generated, sustainable energy needs to be stored for later use, and sustainable energy needs to be used for transportation. And to be effective, the technology used for generation, storage and transportation all need to work together in an integrated way that makes the experience seamless.

Sustainable Energy Future

During the Powerwall 2 and solar roof launch event, we shared our vision for how we can create this integrated sustainable energy future. That vision consists of three pieces. First, there will be a solar roof that will generate sustainable energy from a rooftop that looks better and is more durable than a normal roof, that can be easily customized to fit the unique needs of each house, and that will lower costs to the consumer. Second, the Powerwall 2 storage system, which starts production this quarter at the Gigafactory, will take the energy that is generated by any source (whether from the solar roof, another solar power system, or even the grid) and use it when it's most beneficial, such as during the night, during a power outage, or when the customer can make money by doing so. Third, sustainable energy needs to be used for transportation, which is why electric vehicles are so important.

With these products, our customers will have an entire sustainable energy ecosystem, comprised of products whose benefits go far beyond simply being sustainable. They will be products that like Model S and Model X, you want to show your friends and family because they are so much better than anything you ever had before.

This is our vision for the future – one that is sustainable, less expensive, and just better. We hope you agree that this is a future we should all want.

Solar for Existing Roofs

Savings - Electricity For Less

Use solar energy to power your home and reduce your dependence on the grid. Purchase solar at the lowest price of any national provider with Tesla's price match guarantee and take control of your monthly electricity bill. Learn more about your potential savings in our Design Studio.

Design - Sleek and Durable

Our solar panels are low-profile and durable — quietly converting sunlight to energy for decades to come. Integrated hardware and simple design achieve this by securing the panels close to your roof and to each other for a minimal aesthetic.

Efficiency - Maximum Solar Production

Tesla solar panels are designed to be highly efficient, delivering maximum solar production year-round, even on roofs with complicated angles. Powered by Tesla Solar Inverter, your fully integrated system is safe and reliable.

Experience - 24/7 Monitoring

Manage your solar system from anywhere in the world with 24/7 mobile monitoring. Add a Powerwall to watch your consumption rise and fall in real time, including historical usage.

The Acquisition of SolarCity

Tesla's acquisition of SolarCity is an important part of creating this future. The acquisition will enable us to transform into a truly integrated sustainable energy company capable of developing, producing, selling, installing, and servicing these products in the most seamless way possible.

Tesla has already shown through Model S and Model X, and with our unveiling of Model 3, that the future of automobiles is going to consist exclusively of electric vehicles. People doubted that when we first came out with the Roadster eight years ago, but given the success of Model S and Model X, the overwhelming interest in Model 3, and the fact that other car companies are finally starting electric vehicle programs of their own, no one should doubt that anymore. Every car will ultimately be electric.

Those same naysayers may have similar feelings about solar and storage, but it probably would be unwise to trust them again. Indeed, we are just as confident that the future of energy generation will overwhelmingly consist of solar paired with an integrated storage system.

This is where Tesla's acquisition of SolarCity can make a huge difference. SolarCity is the #1 provider of residential and commercial solar. It maintains a vertically integrated supply chain for high efficiency module manufacturing, it has its own direct sales force, and it has the best installation team in the industry. Moreover, it has figured out how to offer innovative financing options to reduce its cost of capital and make solar energy more accessible and affordable to more customers. The ability to couple all of these advantages with Tesla's design and manufacturing expertise, its global retail footprint, and its loyal customer following provides a unique combination that exceeds what any other company can offer.

Solar Policy

There is clearly overwhelming American public support for policies that support the increased use of residential solar. In late 2015, the Investment Tax Credit, which permits the owner of a solar system to claim 30% of its installed cost as a tax credit, was extended through the end of 2021. An energy storage system, when paired with a solar system, also qualifies for this credit.

Also, a majority of state regulatory bodies have acted to implement and protect net metering, a tariff that quickly and easily encourages adoption of solar. However, leading solar states, acknowledging that net metering as initially implemented will not get us to full societal adoption of solar, have created new policies to encourage the continued growth of solar. California's "NEM 2.0" policy has created a clear migration path to continue to allow solar customers to receive fair compensation for the solar power they produce even as the adoption of solar increases, and implicitly encourages the adoption of battery storage by assigning a higher value to electricity provided when the grid needs it most. The solar and utility industry also reached a landmark deal in New York to encourage sustainable growth of rooftop solar in the state.

A combination of Tesla and SolarCity will create a tightly integrated solar and battery combination that will provide grid-independent, renewable backup power today, and a hedge for customers against future changes to net metering. More significantly, the integration enhances the opportunity for the combined company to sell grid services into the $50 billion per year distribution and transmission market. A number of utilities across the country are beginning to incorporate battery storage to help manage the grid.

SolarCity provides nearly one out of every three new residential solar power systems in the U.S., and now has more than 300,000 installed residential and commercial customers across the country. By combining SolarCity with Tesla, we expect to significantly expand our total addressable market to include a solar market that generates $12 billion in the U.S. alone, and that is expected to grow at a compounded annual growth rate of between 15-20% in the next 5 years. Additionally, with the new products that we have shown, we expect that solar's share of the nation's $400 billion in annual retail electricity sales will increase more than anyone currently expects. And by pairing storage with solar, we can capture a market for our batteries that goes way beyond the market for our cars, thus maximizing the scale and potential of the Gigafactory, where we are developing the world's leading battery technology.

Tesla and SolarCity have a tremendous opportunity to create a vertically integrated sustainable energy company offering end-to-end clean energy products. Leveraging the core competencies of each company, consumers can look forward to deploying and consuming energy in an efficient and sustainable way, with SolarCity's existing solar power systems and ultimately with a solar roof, a Powerwall 2 that maximizes the benefits of the combined system, and a Model S, Model X or Model 3, all while lowering costs and minimizing dependence on fossil fuels and the utility grid.

Starlink

Starlink is a satellite internet constellation being constructed by SpaceX providing satellite Internet access. The constellation will consist of thousands of mass-produced small satellites in low Earth orbit, which communicate with designated ground transceivers.

Engineered by SpaceX

SpaceX is leveraging its experience in building rockets and spacecraft to deploy the world's most advanced broadband internet system. As the world's leading provider of launch services – and the only provider with an orbital class reusable rocket – SpaceX has deep experience with both spacecraft and on-orbit operations

Starlink has now launched more than 500 Starlink satellites to space from reused rockets. Reusability is a key factor toward making the launches as cost-effective as possible.

SpaceX being the launch provider it is rapidly accelerating its Starlink launch program, with 28 launches so far

High-speed, low latency broadband internet.

Starlink is now delivering initial beta service both domestically and internationally, and will continue expansion to near global coverage of the populated world in 2021.

During beta, users can expect to see data speeds vary from 50Mb/s to 150Mb/s and latency from 20ms to 40ms in most locations over the next several months as we enhance the Starlink system. There will also be brief periods of no connectivity at all.

As we launch more satellites, install more ground stations and improve our networking software, data speed, latency and uptime will improve dramatically.

Low latency = video calls & online gaming

Latency is the time it takes to send data from one point to the next. When satellites are far from Earth, latency is high, resulting in poor performance for activities like video calls and online gaming.

Starlink satellites are over 60 times closer to Earth than traditional satellites, resulting in lower latency and the ability to support services typically not possible with traditional satellite internet.

Ideal for rural and remote communities

Starling is ideally suited for areas of the globe where connectivity has typically been a challenge. Unbounded by traditional ground infrastructure Starlink can deliver high-speed broadband internet to locations where access has been unreliable or completely unavailable.

OpenAI

OpenAI is an AI research and deployment company. Our mission is to ensure that artificial general intelligence benefits all of humanity.

OpenAI Charter

We're releasing a charter that describes the principles we use to execute on OpenAI's mission. This document reflects the strategy we've refined over the past two years, including feedback from many people internal and external to OpenAI. The timeline to AGI remains uncertain, but our charter will guide us in acting in the best interests of humanity throughout its development.

OpenAI's mission is to ensure that artificial general intelligence (AGI)—by which we mean highly autonomous systems that outperform humans at most economically valuable work—benefits all of humanity. We will attempt to directly build safe and beneficial AGI, but will also consider our mission fulfilled if our work aids others to achieve this outcome. To that end, we commit to the following principles:

Broadly Distributed Benefits

We commit to use any influence we obtain over AGI's deployment to ensure it is used for the benefit of all, and to avoid enabling uses of AI or AGI that harm humanity or unduly concentrate power.

Our primary fiduciary duty is to humanity. We anticipate needing to marshal substantial resources to fulfill our mission, but will always diligently act to minimize conflicts of interest among our employees and stakeholders that could compromise broad benefit.

Long-Term Safety

We are committed to doing the research required to make AGI safe, and to driving the broad adoption of such research across the AI community.

We are concerned about late-stage AGI development becoming a competitive race without time for adequate safety precautions. Therefore, if a value-aligned, safety-conscious project comes close to building AGI before we do, we commit to stop competing with and start assisting this project. We will work out specifics in case-by-case agreements, but a typical triggering condition might be "a better-than-even chance of success in the next two years."

Technical Leadership

To be effective at addressing AGI's impact on society, OpenAI must be on the cutting edge of AI capabilities—policy and safety advocacy alone would be insufficient.

We believe that AI will have broad societal impact before AGI, and we'll strive to lead in those areas that are directly aligned with our mission and expertise.

Cooperative Orientation

We will actively cooperate with other research and policy institutions; we seek to create a global community working together to address AGI's global challenges.

We are committed to providing public goods that help society navigate the path to AGI. Today this includes publishing most of our AI research, but we expect that safety and security concerns will reduce our traditional publishing in the future, while increasing the importance of sharing safety, policy, and standards research.

Elon Musk's Quotes

"When something is important enough, you do it even if the odds are not in your favor."

"Some people don't like change, but you need to embrace change if the alternative is disaster."

"Failure is an option here. If things are not failing, you are not innovating enough."

"The path to the CEO's office should not be through the CFO's office, and it should not be through the marketing department. It needs to be through engineering and design."

"Persistence is very important. You should not give up unless you are forced to give up."

"I think it's very important to have a feedback loop, where you're constantly thinking about what you've done and how you could be doing it better."

"There's a tremendous bias against taking risks. Everyone is trying to optimize their ass-covering."

"It's OK to have your eggs in one basket as long as you control what happens to that basket."

"Brand is just a perception, and perception will match reality over time. Sometimes it will be ahead, other times it will be behind. But brand is simply a collective impression some have about a product."

"It is a mistake to hire huge numbers of people to get a complicated job done. Numbers will never compensate for talent in getting the right answer (two people who don't know something are no better than one), it will tend to slow down progress, and will make the task incredibly expensive."

"A company is a group organized to create a product or service, and it is only as good as its people and how excited they are about creating. I do want to recognize a ton of super-talented people. I just happen to be the face of the companies."

"People work better when they know what the goal is and why. It is important that people look forward to coming to work in the morning and enjoy working."

"If you're co-founder or CEO, you have to do all kinds of tasks you might not want to do... If you don't do your chores, the company won't succeed... No task is too menial."

"I say something, and then it usually happens. Maybe not on schedule, but it usually happens."

"I do think there is a lot of potential if you have a compelling product and people are willing to pay a premium for that. I think that is what Apple has shown. You can buy a much cheaper cell phone or laptop, but "Apple's product is so much better than the alternative, and people are willing to pay that premium."

"I don't spend my time pontificating about high-concept things; I spend my time solving engineering and manufacturing problems."

"I always invest my own money in the companies that I create. I don't believe in the whole thing of just using other people's money. I don't think that's right. I'm not going to ask other people to invest in something if I'm not prepared to do so myself."

"My biggest mistake is probably weighing too much on someone's talent and not someone's personality. I think it matters whether someone has a good heart."

"I don't create companies for the sake of creating companies, but to get things done."

"I don't believe in process. In fact, when I interview a potential employee and he or she says that 'it's all about the process,' I see that as a bad sign. The problem is that at a lot of big companies, process becomes a substitute for thinking. You're encouraged to behave like a little gear in a complex machine. Frankly, it allows you to keep people who aren't that smart, who aren't that creative."

"Starting and growing a business is as much about the innovation, drive, and determination of the people behind it as the product they sell."

"The first step is to establish that something is possible; then probability will occur."

"There are really two things that have to occur in order for a new technology to be affordable to the mass market. One is you need economies of scale. The other is you need to iterate on the design. You need to go through a few versions."

"Talent is extremely important. It's like a sports team, the team that has the best individual player will often win, but then there's a multiplier from how those players work together and the strategy they employ."

"Work like hell. I mean you just have to put in 80 to 100 hour weeks every week. This improves the odds of success. If other people are putting in 40 hour workweeks and you're putting in 100 hour workweeks, then even if you're doing the same thing, you know that you will achieve in four months what it takes them a year to achieve."

"I've actually not read any books on time management."

“I'm interested in things that change the world or that affect the future and wondrous, new technology where you see it, and you're like, 'Wow, how did that even happen? How is that possible?'“

“Really pay attention to negative feedback and solicit it, particularly from friends. Hardly anyone does that, and it's incredibly helpful.”

“If you get up in the morning and think the future is going to be better, it is a bright day. Otherwise, it's not.”

“What makes innovative thinking happen?... I think it's really a mindset. You have to decide.”

“People should pursue what they're passionate about. That will make them happier than pretty much anything else.”

“Being an entrepreneur is like eating glass and staring into the abyss of death.”

“I wouldn't say I have a lack of fear. In fact, I'd like my fear emotion to be less because it's very distracting and fries my nervous system.”

“If you're trying to create a company, it's like baking a cake. You have to have all the ingredients in the right proportion.”

“I think most of the important stuff on the Internet has been built. There will be continued innovation, for sure, but the great problems of the Internet have essentially been solved.”

“I think we have a duty to maintain the light of consciousness to make sure it continues into the future.”

“When Henry Ford made cheap, reliable cars, people said, 'Nah, what's wrong with a horse?' That was a huge bet he made, and it worked.”

“When somebody has a breakthrough innovation, it is rarely one little thing. Very rarely, is it one little thing. It's usually a whole bunch of things that collectively amount to a huge innovation.”

“You shouldn't do things differently just because they're different. They need to be better.”

“You have to say, 'Well, why did it succeed where others did not?”

“It's very important to like the people you work with, otherwise life andyour job are gonna be quite miserable.”

“We have a strict 'no-assholes policy' at SpaceX.”

“I think the best way to attract venture capital is to try and come up with a demonstration of whatever product or service it is and ideally take that as far as you can. Just see if you can sell that to real customers and start generating some momentum. The further along you can get with that, the more likely you are to get funding."

"Disruptive technology where you really have a big technology discontinuity tends to come from new companies."

"As much as possible, avoid hiring MBAs. MBA programs don't teach people how to create companies."

"Don't delude yourself into thinking something's working when it's not, or you're gonna get fixated on a bad solution."

"If something has to be designed and invented, and you have to figure out how to ensure that the value of the thing you create is greater than the cost of the inputs, then that is probably my core skill."

"I always have optimism, but I'm realistic. It was not with the expectation of great success that I started Tesla or SpaceX... It's just that I thought they were important enough to do anyway."

"It is important to view knowledge as sort of a semantic tree -- make sure you understand the fundamental principles, ie the trunk and big branches, before you get into the leaves/details or there is nothing for them to hang on to."

"You should take the approach that you're wrong. Your goal is to be less wrong."

"You get paid in direct proportion to the difficulty of problems you solve."

"I think it's important to reason from first principles rather than by analogy. The normal way we conduct our lives is we reason by analogy. We are doing this because it's like something else that was done, or it is like what other people are doing. With first principles you boil things down to the most fundamental truths and then up from there."

"Constantly seek criticism. A well thought out critique of whatever you're doing is as valuable as gold."

"It is possible for ordinary people to choose to be extraordinary."

"No, I don't ever give up. I'd have to be dead or completely incapacitated."

"I came to the that we should aspire to increase the scope and scale of human consciousness in order to better understand what questions to ask."

"Any product that needs a manual to work is broken."

"I take the position that I'm always to some degree wrong, and the aspiration is to be less wrong."

“Constantly think about how you could be doing things better.”

“One of the really tough things is figuring out what questions to ask. Once you figure out the question, then the answer is relatively easy.”

“It's OK to have your eggs in one basket as long as you control what happens to that basket.”

“Every person in your company is a vector. Your progress is determined by the sum of all vectors. ”

“I really like computer games, but then if I made really great computer games, how much effect would that have on the world.”

“If you're not concerned about AI safety, you should be. Vastly more risk than North Korea.”

“Life needs to be more than just solving problems every day. You need to wake up and be excited about the future.”

“If something is important enough, you should try even if the outcome is failure.”

“If something is important enough, you should try even if the probable outcome is failure.”

"The only thing that makes sense to do is strive for greater collective enlightenment."

"I think that's the single best piece of advice: Constantly think about how you could be doing things better and questioning yourself."

CPSIA information can be obtained
at www.ICGtesting.com
Printed in the USA
LVHW090412110222
710658LV00003B/6

9 782923 241647